Student Activities
Answer Key

Second Edition

Larry Lemon

bju press®

Greenville, South Carolina

Note:
The fact that materials produced by other publishers may be referred to in this volume does not constitute an endorsement of the content or theological position of materials produced by such publishers. Any references and ancillary materials are listed as an aid to the student or the teacher and in an attempt to maintain the accepted academic standards of the publishing industry.

PRE-ALGEBRA Student Activities Answer Key

Second Edition

Author
Larry Lemon, MS

Contributing Authors
David Brown, PhD
Donna Cherry, MS
Larry Hall, MS
Kathy Kohler, MEd
Kathy Pilger, EdD
Mark Wetzel

Editor
Mary Schleifer

Project Manager
Kevin Neat

Composition
S4 Carlisle Publishing Services

Cover Design
Aaron Dickey
Drew Fields

Technical Consultant
Patricia Tirado, Dzign Associates

ISBN 978-1-59166-999-9 (Answer Key with CD-ROM)

15 14 13 12 11 10 9 8 7 6 5 4

Contents

Chapter 7: Percents

Chapter 8: Applying Equations and Inequalities

Chapter 9: Relations and Functions

Chapter 10: Statistics and Probability

Chapter 11: Radicals

Chapter 12: Geometry

Chapter 13: Area and Volume

Chapter 14: Polynomials

Introduction

Using this manual

The number in parentheses following each activity title in the Contents identifies the section being reviewed or the earliest section for which students have the appropriate background needed to do the activity. You may elect to use an activity at a later time, but it is not recommended that you use it sooner. Some of the activities review several concepts. You may wish to do some of the activities over the course of several days.

Adapting activities to your needs

You need not feel it necessary to cover every activity in this manual. Some may be used for remedial purposes for individual students; others you may wish to do as a class project. You can use parts of an activity without using the entire activity. Some of the activities review more than one section of the text; you may wish to do these in several sections. The purpose of the manual is to provide materials that will be helpful to you. You decide if, when, and how to use the activities.

Types of activities

1. *Enrichment*

   These activities can be done as class projects, assigned to individuals who desire to go beyond the required material, or used as extra credit assignments.

2. *Enhanced Practice*

   These activities contain drill of text material in a disguised fashion or in a way that is different from what is presented in the textbook.

3. *Extra Practice*

   The extra practice activities are basic drill sheets. Many topics covered in the textbook have additional review available through these activities. In addition, the last two activities in each chapter contain more review. The last activity is a cumulative review of any material, primarily from previous chapters. It is preceded by an activity that is an extension of the chapter reviews found at the end of each chapter in the textbook. Besides its use as a review before testing, the chapter review activity could be used as a pretest or as the chapter test itself.

4. *Problem Solving*

   Each chapter has a problem-solving activity. Each activity contains word problems that relate to the chapter material in some way or review previously learned material.

5. *Creation Wonder*

   Each chapter contains a Bible activity that investigates a different aspect of God's creation or how mathematics can be used to fulfill God's command to manage His creation.

6. *Calculator Skill*

   Many of the Calculator Skill activities explain the calculator's keys and their use. The activities offer calculation exercises similar to those in the textbook but for which a calculator is helpful.

Support Materials CD-ROM

The included CD-ROM contains worked-out solutions. Adobe® Reader® is required to view the files and may be downloaded for free at www.adobe.com. Insert the CD-ROM into your CD-ROM drive. If it does not start automatically, open the file listing and click on startup.exe.

1 Integers

Sum Circles (Enhanced Practice; use after 1.2.)

In the following diagram, each large circle contains the sum of the numbers in the smaller circles adjacent to it. For example, the upper right large circle contains a 9. This is the sum of 1 and 8, found in the two adjacent circles.

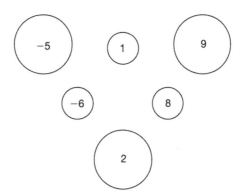

Fill in the missing values in the circles.

1.

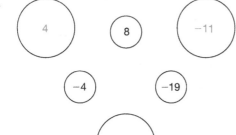

2.

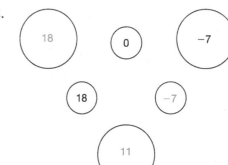

3.

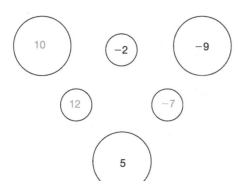

4.

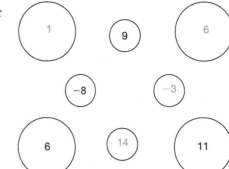

5.

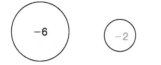

−6 −2 −8
−4 −6
8 12 6

6.

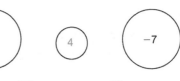

9 4 −7
5 −11
−12 −17 −28

7.

128 116 −106
12 −222
−41 −53 −275

8.

−13 −7 −29
−6 −22
−66 −60 −82

9.

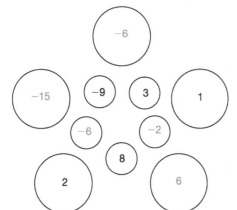

−6
−15 −9 3 1
−6 −2
2 8 6

10.

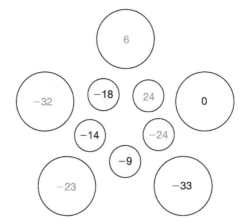

6
−32 −18 24 0
−14 −24
−23 −9 −33

Adding and Subtracting Integers   (Extra Practice; use after 1.3.)

Add.

_____6_____ 1. 9 + (–3)

_____–17_____ 2. –5 + (–12)

_____–11_____ 3. –4 + (–7)

_____3_____ 4. 12 + (–9)

_____–5_____ 5. –12 + 7

_____–5_____ 6. 5 + (–10)

_____1_____ 7. –5 + 6

_____–14_____ 8. –3 + (–11)

_____13_____ 9. 16 + (–3)

_____1_____ 10. –9 + 13 + (–3)

Subtract.

_____17_____ 11. 8 – (–9)

_____6_____ 12. –5 – (–11)

_____–17_____ 13. –12 – 5

_____8_____ 14. 11 – (5 – 2)

_____–2_____ 15. –(8 – 2) – (3 – 7)

_____–8_____ 16. –13 – (–5)

_____8_____ 17. 15 – 7

_____28_____ 18. 21 – (–7)

_____5_____ 19. (8 + 6) – (7 + 2)

_____9_____ 20. –(–5 + 12) – (–13 – 3)

Perform the indicated operations and simplify.

_____11_____ 21. 5 + (–4) – (–6) + 7 + (–3)

_____–55_____ 22. 45 + (–15) – 30 + (–70) – (–10) + 5

_____127_____ 23. –68 + 50 + (–4) – (–28) + 89 – (–32)

_____–8_____ 24. 23 + (–9) + (–7) + 14 + (–29)

_____–22_____ 25. –32 + (–9) + 40 + 8 + (–29)

_____0_____ 26. 10 – 7 – (–4) – 15 – (–8)

_____−43_____ 27. $23 - 18 - 45 - (-8) - 11$

_____5_____ 28. $10 + 11 + (-12) - (-13) + 14 + (-15) - 16$

_____2_____ 29. $64 - 32 - 16 - 8 - 4 - 2$

_____5_____ 30. $|3 - 8|$

_____5_____ 31. $|8 - 3|$

_____11_____ 32. $|-3 - 8|$

_____1_____ 33. $|9 - 13| - |-11 + 8|$

_____19_____ 34. $|16 - 9| + |-7 - 5|$

_____4_____ 35. $|-6 + (-11) - (-5)| - |12 - 7 + (-13)|$

Make a Conjecture

Use several examples to answer the following questions. Include both positive and negative integers in your examples for exercises 36 and 37.

_____yes_____ 36. Does $|a - b| = |b - a|$?

_____≤_____ 37. Which symbol ($\leq$, $=$, or $\geq$) should be inserted into the following sentence: $|a + b|$? $|a| + |b|$?

_____yes_____ 38. If x is a negative integer, is it true that $|x| = -x$?

_____10 or −2_____ 39. If $|x - 4| = 6$, what possible values of x make this equation true?

40. If $|x - 4| = 6$, what two equations would you solve to obtain the answers found in exercise 39?
$x - 4 = 6$ and $x - 4 = -6$

Clock Arithmetic (Enrichment; use after 1.3.)

A number line is often used for adding and subtracting integers. For example, $-4 + 3$ can be illustrated on a number line, as pictured to the right.

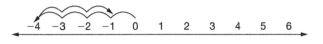

Instead of a number line, a circle can be used to do arithmetic. This type of arithmetic is often known as clock, or modular, arithmetic. Three hours after 8:00 is 11:00. However, the clock is different from the number line in that it is cyclic—it repeats the same cycle of numbers over and over. Clock arithmetic uses only twelve numbers, unlike the number line, which uses an infinite number.

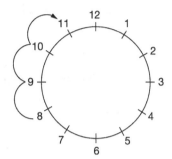

The problem to the right is symbolized as $8 +_{12} 3 = 11$. The subscript 12 indicates that a twelve-hour clock is being used.

An interesting aspect of clock arithmetic occurs when the sum exceeds 12. In the problem $10 +_{12} 4$, when you start at 10 on the circle and add 4, the sum is 2. Therefore, $10 +_{12} 4 = 2$.

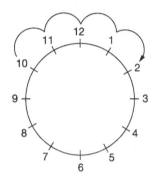

How can clock arithmetic be done without having to count using the face of a clock? Suppose you want to add $6 +_{12} 8$. Add the integers: $6 + 8 = 14$. Then subtract 12 from the sum, since the cycle repeats after reaching 12 on the clock: $14 - 12 = 2$. Therefore, $6 +_{12} 8 = 2$. This procedure is used in clock arithmetic whenever the sum is greater than 12. Consider these additional examples:

$3 +_{12} 11 = 2$, since $3 + 11 = 14$ and $14 - 12 = 2$.

$10 +_{12} 6 = 4$, since $10 + 6 = 16$ and $16 - 12 = 4$.

Clock subtraction follows the same concept as integer subtraction. Subtracting an integer is equivalent to adding the opposite: $3 - 8 = 3 + (-8) = -5$. The *opposite* of an integer is the number that is the same distance from zero, but on the opposite side of zero on the number line. It is also called the *additive inverse*. 8 and -8 are opposites. The sum of opposites is zero: $8 + (-8) = 0$.

So what are opposites in clock arithmetic? There are no negative numbers on the face of a clock, and there is no zero. But in clock arithmetic 12 is similar to 0. Adding 12 to 9 in clock arithmetic brings you back to 9 on the clock: $9 +_{12} 12 = 9$.

In clock arithmetic, opposites are numbers that add up to equal 12. Therefore, the opposite of 8 is 4. The opposite of 2 is 10. You can do subtraction in clock arithmetic in the same manner that you subtract integers— add the opposite: $5 -_{12} 8 = 5 +_{12} 4 = 9$.

Find the following sums in clock arithmetic.

_____10_____ 1. $9 +_{12} 1$

_____11_____ 2. $6 +_{12} 5$

_____1_____ 3. $4 +_{12} 9$

_____7_____ 4. $10 +_{12} 9$

_____3_____ 5. $8 +_{12} 7$

_____5_____ 6. $11 +_{12} 6$

State the opposite of the following clock arithmetic numbers.

_____4_____ 7. 8

_____6_____ 8. 6

_____1_____ 9. 11

_____10_____ 10. 2

Convert each of the following clock subtraction problems to an equivalent clock addition problem; then solve.

_____$9 +_{12} 7 = 4$_____ 11. $9 -_{12} 5$

_____$3 +_{12} 2 = 5$_____ 12. $3 -_{12} 10$

_____$5 +_{12} 10 = 3$_____ 13. $5 -_{12} 2$

_____$4 +_{12} 10 = 2$_____ 14. $4 -_{12} 2$

_____$10 +_{12} 4 = 2$_____ 15. $10 -_{12} 8$

_____$3 +_{12} 4 = 7$_____ 16. $3 -_{12} 8$

_____$7 +_{12} 1 = 8$_____ 17. $7 -_{12} 11$

_____$1 +_{12} 3 = 4$_____ 18. $1 -_{12} 9$

_____$6 +_{12} 2 = 8$_____ 19. $6 -_{12} 10$

_____$4 +_{12} 5 = 9$_____ 20. $4 -_{12} 7$

Chapter 1

Multiplying and Dividing Integers (Extra Practice; use after 1.5.)

Multiply.

_____28_____ 1. $4 \cdot 7$

_____−66_____ 3. -6×11

_____−391_____ 5. $-23 \cdot 17$

_____−84_____ 7. $-7 \cdot 12$

_____−2,079_____ 9. $-9(-11)(-3)(7)$

_____−65_____ 2. $5(-13)$

_____120_____ 4. $-8(-15)$

_____−18_____ 6. -2×9

_____560_____ 8. $16(-5)(-7)$

_____168_____ 10. $-4(-1)(-6)(-7)$

Divide.

_____4_____ 11. $-76 \div (-19)$

_____−20_____ 13. $\dfrac{-120}{6}$

_____−4_____ 15. $\dfrac{12 - (-8)}{-5}$

_____−13_____ 17. $169 \div (-13)$

_____−16_____ 19. $\dfrac{-6(-8)}{-3}$

_____8_____ 12. $-56 \div (-7)$

_____17_____ 14. $\dfrac{-221}{-13}$

_____−7_____ 16. $-84 \div (2 \cdot 6)$

_____8_____ 18. $-\dfrac{224}{-28}$

_____2_____ 20. $-84 \div 6 \div (-7)$

Perform the indicated operations and simplify.

_____−2_____ 21. $-36 \div (-9) \div (-2)$

_____−80_____ 22. $-48 \div (-3) \times (-5)$

_____4_____ 23. $-12 \times 5 \div (-3) \div 5$

_____6_____ 24. $\dfrac{18(-3)}{-9}$

_____128_____ 25. $16 \cdot (-72 \div 9) \div 8(-8)$

_____ −60 _____ 26. $\dfrac{3(-16)}{4} \cdot 5$

_____ 6 _____ 27. $33 \div (-11) \cdot (-30) \div 15$

_____ −168 _____ 28. $\dfrac{-24}{-5(16) \div 20} \cdot (-28)$

_____ 1,100 _____ 29. $-5(-14)(11) \div (-7)(-10)$

_____ 32 _____ 30. $80 \div (-5) \times (-4) \div 2$

_____ −9,240 _____ 31. $-15 \times 11 \times (-7) \times 4 \times (-2)$

_____ 2 _____ 32. $\dfrac{-8(7)}{-14(2)}$

_____ 384 _____ 33. $-3[-96 \div (-3)(-12) \div 3]$

_____ −1 _____ 34. $\dfrac{-672 \div 21}{1{,}024 \div 8 \div 4}$

_____ −280 _____ 35. $144 \div (-6) \times (-5) \div (-3) \times 7$

_____ 600 _____ 36. $40 \times \dfrac{-4(15)}{-8 \div 2}$

Make a Conjecture

For each statement, choose one of the options in parentheses.

_____ negative _____ 37. If a problem containing only multiplication and division has three negative numbers, the answer will be (negative/positive).

_____ positive _____ 38. If a problem containing only multiplication and division has four negative numbers, the answer will be (negative/positive).

_____ odd _____ 39. If a problem contains only multiplication and division, the answer is negative if the equation contains an (even/odd) number of negative integers.

_____ even _____ 40. If a problem contains only multiplication and division, the answer is positive if the equation contains an (even/odd) number of negative integers.

Problem Solving (Use after 1.7.)

Solve the following problems by using the four-point checklist.

1. **Read** to understand the question and identify the needed data.
2. **Plan** what to do to solve the problem.
3. **Solve** the problem by carrying out the plan.
4. **Check** to make sure the solution is reasonable.

1. A construction company is working on a project that requires the temperature to be above 38°F. The weather bureau has warned of a cold front moving into the area with temperatures dropping four degrees per hour for the next twelve hours. If it is 66°F at 9 AM, at what time will the project need to be completed?

   4 PM

2. Find the time from exercise 1 when the temperature reaches freezing (32°F). Also find the lowest temperature expected later that night.

   freezing: between 5 PM and 6 PM; after 12 hr. (9 PM): 18°F

3. A certain area of Siberia has temperature extremes from 98°F in midsummer to –94°F in the coldest part of winter. What is the difference, or range, of temperatures for this area?

   192°F

4. Lisa's grandma had an extensive collection of salt and pepper shakers that she decided to give away to her granddaughters and nieces. She gave half of them to Lisa. Of those remaining she gave half to another granddaughter, Jennifer. Then she gave half of those remaining to her niece Rachel. Finally, half of those remaining went to another niece, Kelly. If Lisa's grandma still has 35 of her favorites remaining, how many were in the original collection?

   560

5. Josh is planning to paint the walls and ceilings in several rooms of his home. The walls have a combined area of 1,840 ft.². The ceilings have a combined area of 920 ft.². The walls will require two coats of paint, and the ceilings will take a single coat of paint. Each gallon of paint covers about 240 ft.². How many gallons of paint are needed for the walls? How many gallons are needed for the ceilings? Round up to the next whole gallon if necessary.

   walls: 16 gal.; ceilings: 4 gal.

6. Josh has checked some prices for quality interior latex paint. He found that ceiling paint costs $25/gal. and wall paint costs $28/gal. He will also need a new roller and pan set that sells for $18.50, a package of smooth wall rollers costing $12, and a package of brushes that is $15.75. Based on your answers to exercise 5, what will it cost him to paint these rooms?

$594.25

7. The Dow Jones Industrial Average started a certain week at 12,642.21, and during the week the following changes occurred in the value of the market. Find the value of the Dow at the close on Friday.

Day	Monday	Tuesday	Wednesday	Thursday	Friday
Change	+102.45	−87.25	−124.38	+23.60	+95.42

12,652.05

8. Jose needed to know how many integers are between 10 and 100, not including those two numbers. He also needed to find their sum: $11 + 12 + \ldots + 99$. He liked the idea of adding small numbers rather than adding large numbers. Therefore, he started out by adding $11 + 99$. Then he added $12 + 98$. He was surprised by what happened. What were the sums of each pair of numbers Jose added? How many numbers are between 10 and 100, not including 10 and 100? Determine a shortcut to find the sum. What is the final sum?

110; 89; 89(110) ÷ 2 = 4,895

9. Jose has another project that requires him to find the sum of the multiples of three from 3 all the way to 999, including those two numbers. If he uses the small number plus large number method that he discovered in exercise 8, what is the sum of the multiples of three from 3 to 999? Note that he will also need to know how many numbers he has in order to use that method.

$\frac{999 - 3}{3} + 1 = 166{,}833$

10. Andrew has the following records for his batting in the county baseball league. Batting average is calculated by dividing the number of hits by the number of times at bat and then writing the result as a decimal to the nearest thousandth. What is Andrew's batting average at this point in the season?

Game	1	2	3	4	5	6	7	8	9	10	11	12
Hits	2	1	4	3	1	2	0	0	3	3	2	2
At bats	5	3	4	5	4	4	3	3	5	4	4	5

.469

Calculator Skill 1 (Use after 1.7.)

written for the TI-30Xa

If this is your first experience with the TI-30Xa, you will need to spend a little time becoming familiar with the calculator keys. This is a scientific calculator, so it is designed to do computations that relate to math and science. Some keys will not be used in the activities in this text, such as the trigonometry functions and their inverses. Note that most of the second function keys are functions that are preprogrammed for this calculator. Also, since this is an algebraic calculator, the order of operations used in algebra is done automatically.

Order of Operations

In order to gain an understanding of how the calculator performs the order of operations, work through the following examples. Then check the process by applying the definition of the order of operations. Before doing so, review the order of operations applied in algebra.

Order of Operations
First, perform all operations within grouping symbols.
Evaluate all terms with exponents in the order they occur from left to right.
Perform all multiplications and divisions in the order they occur from left to right.
Finally, perform all additions and subtractions in the order they occur from left to right.

Example 1
Calculate $18 \div 6 \times 5 - 2 \times 9 \div 3 + 12 \times 5 \div 3$.

Answer
The calculator keystrokes are $18 \div 6 \times 5 - 2 \times 9 \div 3 + 12 \times 5 \div 3 =$. The result is 29.

It may seem as though the calculator is not following the order of operations, but if you watch the screen you will see that the calculator did $(18 \div 6 \times 5) - (2 \times 9 \div 3) + (12 \times 5 \div 3) = 15 - 6 + 20 = 29$. So we see that the calculator followed the order of operations precisely.

Inserting symbols of grouping into a numerical expression may change the answer. The TI-30Xa has a pair of parentheses located near the center of the calculator. Use these keys to place a numerical string within symbols of grouping.

Example 2
Calculate $\dfrac{16}{2+6}$.

Answer
The calculator keystrokes are $16 \div (2 + 6) =$. The result is 2.

Notice that the entire denominator needs to be placed inside parentheses since 16 is being divided by the sum of 2 and 6.

Perform the indicated operations using your calculator.

_____93_____   1. $24 \div 3 \times 5 \div 2 - 3 \times (8 - 11) + 80 \div 5 \times 4$

_____24_____   2. $(24 - 3 \times 2) \cdot (14 \times 2 + 8) \div 27$

_____9_____   3. $(24 \div 2 \times 11 \div 4 - 12 \times 3 + 5 \times 15) \div 8$

_____−12_____   4. $\dfrac{5 \times (23 - 3 \times 9)}{16 \div 2 - 9 \times 2} - 4 \times 7 \div 2$

_____3,080_____   5. $(3 \times 5 + 7) \cdot (4 \times 6 - 14) \cdot (5 \times 7 - 21)$

_____58_____   6. $60 - [(5 + 2) - (12 - 7)]$

_____5_____   7. $56 \div (4 \times 2 - 3 \times 5) + 13$

_____−15_____   8. $(18 \div 3 \times 4) \div 8 \times (-5)$

_____59_____   9. $64 - \dfrac{(3 \times 5 + 2 \times 8) + 9}{(19 - 7 \times 2) \div 5 \times 8}$

_____239_____   10. $240 - 120 \div 30 \div 2^2$

Creation Wonders—Revelation of the Stars (Bible Activity; use after 1.8.)

Psalm 19:1 exhorts us to wonder at all the created universe when it proclaims, "The heavens declare the glory of God; and the firmament sheweth His handywork." Those things that can be observed around us are known as *general revelation*. The information that God sets down in the Scriptures is called *special revelation*. Romans 1:19–20 makes it clear that what we observe in the universe speaks about a sovereign Creator: "Because that which may be known of God is manifest in them; for God hath shewed it unto them. For the invisible things of him from the creation of the world are clearly seen, being understood by the things that are made, even his eternal power and Godhead; so that they are without excuse."

1. Read the account of creation in Genesis 1:1–31 and Hebrews 1:1–3. According to these passages, how did God create?
   He spoke everything into existence.

2. Astronomers do not know how many stars exist, but what they do know is that the number is billions of billions. In light of these huge numbers, what do Psalm 147:4 and Isaiah 40:26 tell us that the vast array of stars says about the Creator?
   He is all-knowing (omniscient) and all-powerful (omnipotent).

The closest stars to our solar system are a system of three stars called Alpha Centauri A, B, and C. Alpha Centauri C (Proxima) is the dimmest and yet closest to our solar system. It is 4.22 light-years away. A light-year is the distance light travels in one year.

3. If light travels at approximately 186,000 mi./sec., how long would it take a spaceship traveling at 50,000 mi./hr. to make the trip from Earth to Alpha Centauri C? (Hint: First find how many miles light travels in one year, and then find how many miles the spaceship travels in one year.)
   56,514.56 yr.

In Isaiah 42:5 we read that God "created the heavens, and stretched them out." The question arises, how much did God stretch the heavens out? Our sun lies in the Milky Way galaxy, a spiral galaxy with a diameter of about 100,000 light-years that contains more than 200 billion stars. Within the Local Group of our galaxy there are three large galaxies and more than thirty smaller ones. At the other end of our group lies the Andromeda galaxy, at 180,000 light-years in diameter and 2,900,000 light-years away. This is just the close part of the heavens; there are hundreds of billions of other galaxies beyond!

4. Assume that the average number of stars in each galaxy of our Local Group matches the Milky Way. Write in scientific notation the total number of stars in the approximately thirty-three galaxies of this Local Group.
   6.6×10^{12} stars

Thou, even thou, art Lord alone; thou hast made heaven, the heaven of heavens, with all their host, the earth, and all things that are therein, the seas, and all that is therein, and thou preservest them all; and the host of heaven worshippeth thee. Nehemiah 9:6

Chapter 1 Review

Write T for true or F for false. If the statement is false, correct it.

___F___ 1. All integers are either positive or negative.
Every nonzero integer is either positive or negative.

___F___ 2. Integers with opposite signs have the same absolute value.
Opposites (additive inverses) have the same absolute value.

___T___ 3. If an integer is negative, its absolute value is also its additive inverse.

___F___ 4. The sum of two integers with the same sign is always positive.
The sum of two integers with the same sign has the same sign as the integers.

___T___ 5. The product of three negative integers is always negative.

___F___ 6. Powers of negative integers are always negative.
Odd powers of negative integers are always negative.

Tell which integer has the larger absolute value.

___22___ 7. −18 or 22

___−41___ 8. −38 or −41

___−105___ 9. 104 or −105

___$-\frac{1}{10^4}$___ 10. $-\frac{1}{10^4}$ or $-\frac{1}{10^5}$

Perform the indicated operations and simplify.

___9___ 11. −8 + 17

___−27___ 12. −14 − 13

___20___ 13. 8 − (−12)

___15___ 14. −7 + 37 + (−15)

___9___ 15. 16 − (12 − 5)

___−48___ 16. 12 · (−4)

___4___ 17. 48 ÷ 4 ÷ 3

___80___ 18. −20(12 − 16)

_____17_____ 19. $\dfrac{34 \times (-3)}{-6}$

_____1_____ 20. $\dfrac{8 - (-14) + 3}{25}$

_____52_____ 21. $21 + (-8) - (-5) + 51 - 17$

_____3_____ 22. $|5 - 22| - |-19 + 5|$

_____31_____ 23. $|16 - (-8) + (-11)| + |-18|$

_____32_____ 24. $-24(-12)(3) \div 27$

_____3_____ 25. $42 \div (-7) \times (-8) \div 16$

_____-6_____ 26. $-3(-6)(-5) - (-7)(12)$

_____-32_____ 27. $(24 \div 3)[64 \div (-16)]$

_____5_____ 28. $-81 \div (-3) \times 15 \div (120 - 39)$

_____4_____ 29. $\dfrac{448 \div (-16)}{91 \div (-13)}$

_____-16_____ 30. $-27 + \dfrac{-3(9 - 31)}{-2(-45 + 42)}$

Write in exponential form without fractions.

_____a^4_____ 31. $a \cdot a \cdot a \cdot a$

_____x^{-6}_____ 32. $\dfrac{1}{x \cdot x} \cdot \dfrac{1}{x \cdot x \cdot x \cdot x}$

Simplify the following. Leave the answers in exponential form.

_____5^{11}_____ 33. $5^3 \cdot 5^8$

_____b^{17}_____ 34. $b^2 \cdot b^9 \cdot b^6$

_____$27y^6$_____ 35. $(3y^2)^3$

_____x^3y^4_____ 36. $\dfrac{x^7y^5}{x^4y}$

Write the following numbers in scientific notation.

_____8.23×10^6_____ 37. 8,230,000

_____4.9×10^{-5}_____ 38. 0.000049

Write the following numbers in standard form.

_____-0.0000000261_____ 39. -2.61×10^{-8}

_____-3,100,000_____ 40. -3.1×10^6

Cumulative Review 1

_____c_____ 1. Evaluate $-[34 + (-16) - 12]$.
- a. 16
- b. −16
- c. −6
- d. 6
- e. none of these

_____d_____ 2. Evaluate $15 + 16 + (-17) - (-18) + 19 + (-20) - 21 + (-25)$.
- a. −25
- b. −33
- c. −5
- d. −15
- e. none of these

_____b_____ 3. Evaluate $|-12 + (-24) - 4| - |42 - 25 - (-28)|$.
- a. 5
- b. −5
- c. 95
- d. −95
- e. none of these

_____e_____ 4. Evaluate $-64 \div 4 \times (-9) \times 5$.
- a. 144
- b. −720
- c. 16
- d. −144
- e. none of these

_____a_____ 5. Evaluate $\frac{5 \cdot (-21) \cdot 3}{45} \cdot (-11)$.
- a. 77
- b. −7
- c. 7
- d. −315
- e. none of these

_____c_____ 6. Evaluate $5 \times (-6) \times 15 - 3 + (-8) \times (-4)$.
- a. 421
- b. −485
- c. −421
- d. −328
- e. none of these

_____b_____ 7. Evaluate $(-3^2 + 2^3)^2$.
- a. −17
- b. 1
- c. −1
- d. 289
- e. none of these

_____b_____ 8. Simplify $\frac{x^5}{x^2}$.
- a. x^{-3}
- b. x^3
- c. x^2
- d. x^{-2}
- e. none of these

_____c_____ 9. Write 34,561.28 in scientific notation.
    a. 3.456128×10^{-4} d. 3.456128×10^{6}
    b. 3.456128×10^{-6} e. none of these
    c. 3.456128×10^{4}

_____d_____ 10. Write 8.545×10^{-4} in standard form.
    a. 85,450   d. 0.0008545
    b. 8,545   e. none of these
    c. 0.00008545

_____a_____ 11. Kathy chose two successive multiples of 4. Their sum is 108, and their product is 2,912. Which of the following pairs did she choose?
    a. 52 and 56   d. 48 and 52
    b. 4 and 104   e. none of these
    c. 28 and 104

_____b_____ 12. Write $\dfrac{8y^4}{2y^9}$ in exponential form without fractions.
    a. $4y^{-4}$ d. $6y^{-5}$
    b. $4y^{-5}$ e. none of these
    c. $6y^{5}$

_____a_____ 13. Which integer has the largest absolute value?
    a. −35   d. 22
    b. −32   e. none of these
    c. 33

_____d_____ 14. Which integer has the smallest absolute value?
    a. −35   d. 22
    b. −32   e. none of these
    c. 33

_____c_____ 15. Evaluate $68 \div 4 \times 2 - 6 \times 9 \div 3 \div 2 + 18$.
    a. 60   d. 25
    b. 21.75   e. none of these
    c. 43

2 Expressions

Creation Wonders—Invisible Things   (Bible Activity; use after 2.1.)

In Colossians 1:16–17 the apostle Paul adds the following comment to a description of Christ's redemptive work: "For by him were all things created, that are in heaven, and that are in earth, visible and invisible, whether they be thrones, or dominions, or principalities, or powers: all things were created by him, and for him: and he is before all things, and by him all things consist." Just as we can look into the heavens with a telescope, we can also look into the universe of invisible things with a microscope. Of course, some of the invisible things, such as atoms, are even too small to see with a microscope. But the Scriptures tell us in Hebrews 11:3 that the visible world of matter is made of invisible things.

1. According to Hebrews 11:3, what is the basis for accepting and understanding God's role as the Creator of all things?
   faith

God's basic building blocks for all matter are called atoms. The atom is the smallest degree to which a substance can be divided and still retain its properties. In our daily lives we are better acquainted with molecules, such as water, salt, or oxygen, but each of these is made up of atoms bound together in special ways. In the atomic realm things are extremely small, just as they are extremely large in the realm of stars and planets.

2. If an atom is about 5×10^{-8} mm in diameter, and a hyphen is 1 mm long, how many atoms would you have to line up to equal the length of a hyphen?
   20,000,000 atoms

Each atom consists of three basic parts—protons, neutrons, and electrons. The nucleus is made up of protons and neutrons with an electron cloud around the nucleus. Relative to the sizes of the particles, the electron cloud is a great distance away from the nucleus. Protons and neutrons have enormous mass compared to electrons; they are about two thousand times more massive than electrons.

3. If 56 g of iron atoms contains about 6.02×10^{23} atoms, what is the mass in grams of one atom of iron?
   9.3×10^{-23} g

The diameter of an atom is determined by where its electrons are located.

4. Assume that the nucleus of the atom in exercise 2 is about 1.6×10^{-12} mm in diameter. If one atom is enlarged so that its nucleus is 10 cm, or 100 mm, find the atom's diameter. (Hint: Use a proportion to solve. Let the ratios compare the size of the diameter to the size of the nucleus.)
   3,125,000 mm

Through faith we understand that the worlds were framed by the word of God, so that things which are seen were not made of things which do appear. Hebrews 11:3

Properties of Addition (Extra Practice; use after 2.1.)

Identify whether a property of addition (Identity, Inverse, Associative, or Commutative) or the definition of subtraction is used to go from the left to the right side of each equation.

Associative   1. $9 + (-3 + 7) = [9 + (-3)] + 7$

Commutative   2. $-5 + (-12 + 3) = (-12 + 3) + (-5)$

Inverse   3. $(-4 + 4) + y = 0 + y$

Associative   4. $12 + (-9 + 2) = [12 + (-9)] + 2$

Commutative   5. $(-12 + 7) + 9 = [7 + (-12)] + 9$

definition of subtraction   6. $(8 - 9) + (-5) = [(8 + (-9)] - 5$

Identity   7. $-5 + (-11) + 0 = -5 + (-11)$

Inverse   8. $[x + (-x)] + z = z$

definition of subtraction   9. $(14 - 28)x = [14 + (-28)]x$

Associative   10. $(x - 15) + 3 = x + (-15 + 3)$

Inverse   11. $18[z + 9 + (-9)] = 18(z + 0)$

Make a Conjecture

_no_   12. Is the set $\{0, 1\}$ closed for addition? Remember that closure requires every sum of two numbers in a set to have an answer that is in the set.

yes   13. Is the set of positive even integers closed for addition?

_no_   14. Is the set of negative odd integers closed for addition?

15. For an addition statement $a + b$, the terms are both called _addends_. Why do the terms in the subtraction expression $a - b$ have different names? What are those names?
    Subtraction is not commutative, so the order is important; $a - b \neq b - a$. In the statement $a - b$, the number a is called the minuend, and the number b is called the subtrahend.

Properties of Multiplication   (Extra Practice; use after 2.2.)

Identify which property of multiplication (Associative, Closure, Commutative, Identity, or Zero) is used to go from the left to the right side of each equation.

_____Closure_____ 1. $12 \times 4 = 48$; 48 is an integer.

_____Commutative_____ 2. $12 \times 4 = 4 \times 12$

_____Associative_____ 3. $-3(8 \cdot 13) = (-3 \cdot 8)13$

_____Zero_____ 4. $3(8 \cdot 0) = 0$

_____Commutative_____ 5. $-5[6 + (-11)] = [6 + (-11)](-5)$

_____Identity_____ 6. $-18 \cdot (10 \cdot 1) = -18 \cdot 10$

_____Associative_____ 7. $(x - 5)[(x + 12)(2x - 6)] = [(x - 5)(x + 12)] \cdot (2x - 6)$

_____Identity_____ 8. $(64 \cdot 1) \cdot (81 \cdot 5) = 64 \cdot (81 \cdot 5)$

_____Commutative_____ 9. $x \cdot (y^2 \cdot z^3) = (z^3 \cdot y^2) \cdot x$

_____Associative_____ 10. $x(-5 \cdot 4) = -5x \cdot 4$

_____Zero_____ 11. $16b(-5c)(0)(-21b) = 0$

_____Associative_____ 12. $7(2x) + 9(5x) + 11(3x) = 14x + 45x + 33x$

Make a Conjecture

_____yes_____ 13. Is the set $\{0, 1\}$ closed for multiplication?

_____yes_____ 14. Is the set of even integers closed for multiplication?

_____yes_____ 15. Is the set of odd integers closed for multiplication?

The Distributive Property (Enhanced Practice; use after 2.3.)

Use the Distributive Property to find the value of each variable.

_____$m = 9$_____ 1. $5(9 + 13) = 5m + 5(13)$

_____$x = 3$_____ 2. $x(21 - 16) = 3 \cdot 21 - 3 \cdot 16$

_____$y = 10$_____ 3. $(y + 18) \cdot 5 = 10 \cdot 5 + 18 \cdot 5$

_____$c = -7$_____ 4. $(9 + 6)(-7) = 9(-7) + 6c$

_____$a = 5; b = -3$_____ 5. $10(a + b) = 10 \cdot 5 + 10 \cdot (-3)$

_____$w = -9$_____ 6. $7(-6 + w) = -42 + 7 \cdot (-9)$

_____$a = 2; b = 9; c = -4$_____ 7. $a(b + c) = 2 \cdot 9 + 2 \cdot (-4)$

_____$x = 15; y = 3; z = 14$_____ 8. $(y + z)x = 3x + 14 \cdot 15$

Use the Distributive Property to write an equivalent expression.

_____$6 \cdot 5 - 6 \cdot 3$_____ 9. $6(5 - 3)$ _____$-7 \cdot 5 + 12 \cdot 5$_____ 10. $(-7 + 12)5$

_____$-9 \cdot 8 + 9 \cdot 3$_____ 11. $-9(8 - 3)$ _____$(9 + 16)2$_____ 12. $9 \cdot 2 + 16 \cdot 2$

_____$8 \cdot 3 + 3c$_____ 13. $(8 + c)3$ _____$5w - 19w$_____ 14. $(5 - 19)w$

Make a Conjecture

15. Does division distribute over addition? For example, does $(6 + 4) \div 2$ equal $(6 \div 2) + (4 \div 2)$? Is this always true? Do some examples, and then write your conjecture in the form of a variable expression.
    Yes, it is true. Therefore, $(a + b) \div c = (a \div c) + (b \div c)$.

16. Would the Distributive Property be true if a number is divided by a sum? For example, does $a \div (b + c) = (a \div b) + (a \div c)$? Do some examples to verify your conclusion.
    No. Example: $a = 18$, $b = 6$, and $c = 3$; $18 \div (6 + 3) = 18 \div 9 = 2$, but $(18 \div 6) + (18 \div 3) = 3 + 6 = 9$.

Algebraic Proofs (Enrichment; use after 2.3.)

A proof is a step-by-step reasoning process showing a statement to be true. Each statement must have a reason. Use the following procedures when writing a proof.

1. Start with two columns, one for the statements and one for the reasons.

2. List the left side of the equation. The reason for this statement is "given."

3. Work to change the left side to match the right side, using properties of algebra.

Example
Prove $3x + 4(2x) + 8 = 3x + 8(x + 1)$.

Answer

Statement	Reason
1. $3x + 4(2x) + 8$	1. given
2. $= 3x + (4 \cdot 2)x + 8$	2. Associative Property
3. $= 3x + 8x + 8$	3. arithmetic
4. $= 3x + 8(x + 1)$	4. Distributive Property

Complete the proof by supplying the reasons: $2h + 3(4 + h) = 3h + 2(6 + h)$.

Statement	Reason
1. $2h + 3(4 + h)$	1. given
2. $= 2h + 12 + 3h$	2. Distributive Property
3. $= 3h + 2h + 12$	3. Commutative Property
4. $= 3h + 12 + 2h$	4. Commutative Property
5. $= 3h + 2(6 + h)$	5. Distributive Property

Make a proof table to prove $4y + 3x + 8y + 18 = 4(3y) + 3(x + 6)$.

Statement	Reason
1. $4y + 3x + 8y + 18$	1. given
2. $= 4y + 8y + 3x + 18$	2. Commutative Property
3. $= (4 + 8)y + 3(x + 6)$	3. Distributive Property
4. $= 12y + 3(x + 6)$	4. arithmetic
5. $= (4 \cdot 3)y + 3(x + 6)$	5. factors of 12
6. $= 4(3y) + 3(x + 6)$	6. Associative Property

Step 3 can be done in two separate statements with the same reason for each.

Calculator Skill 2 (Use after 2.4.)

written for the TI-30Xa

Evaluating Expressions

Jennifer: How am I going to do my homework? My calculator's division and subtraction buttons won't work, and we don't have time tonight to buy a new one.

Jason: You don't need a division button, or a subtraction button for that matter. Just use the reciprocal button, $\boxed{1/x}$, and multiply for division. In the case of subtraction, use the $\boxed{+\!\leftcirc\!-}$ button, which changes the sign of the number, and add.

If Jennifer had come to you for advice, would you have known how to help her? Jason gave her a means of doing her homework with only two of the operation buttons working. He was able to do this because he remembered that every division problem is a multiplication problem and every subtraction problem is an addition problem.

Division is multiplying by the reciprocal (multiplicative inverse). For example, $x \div y = x \cdot \frac{1}{y}$.

Subtraction is adding the opposite (additive inverse). For example, $x - y = x + (-y)$.

Example 1
Evaluate the expression $\frac{240}{5 \cdot 13 + 15} + 64 \cdot 3$ without using the division button or the memory registers.

Answer
Use the following keystrokes on your calculator: 5 $\boxed{\times}$ 13 $\boxed{+}$ 15 $\boxed{=}$ $\boxed{1/x}$ $\boxed{\times}$ 240 $\boxed{+}$ 64 $\boxed{\times}$ 3 $\boxed{=}$. The result is 195.

After the equal sign is pushed the first time, 80 appears in the display. The $\boxed{1/x}$ button gives the reciprocal of 80. This is the same as $\frac{1}{5 \cdot 13 + 15}$, which is then multiplied times 240.

Example 2
Evaluate the expression $56 - 17 + 34 - 8$ without using the subtraction button.

Answer
Use the following keystrokes on your calculator: 56 $\boxed{+}$ 17 $\boxed{+\!\leftcirc\!-}$ $\boxed{+}$ 34 $\boxed{+}$ 8 $\boxed{+\!\leftcirc\!-}$ $\boxed{=}$. The result is 65.

To enter a negative number into your calculator, you must enter a positive number and then place a negative sign in front of it by using the $\boxed{+\!\leftcirc\!-}$ button. Do not use the subtraction button, $\boxed{-}$.

Example 3
Evaluate the expression $(48 - 20) \div 7$ without using the $\boxed{\div}$ or the $\boxed{-}$ button.

Answer
Use the following keystrokes on your calculator: $\boxed{(}$ 48 $\boxed{+}$ 20 $\boxed{+\!\leftcirc\!-}$ $\boxed{)}$ $\boxed{\times}$ 7 $\boxed{1/x}$ $\boxed{=}$. The result is 4.

Perform the following calculations without using the division or subtraction buttons or the memory registers.

_____26_____ 1. $32 - (18 \div 3)$

_____47_____ 2. $82 - 14 - 12 - 9$

_____14_____ 3. $6 \times 9 \div 3 - 16 \div 4$

_____−1_____ 4. $\dfrac{8 - 19}{5 \times 3 - 12 \div 3}$

_____$0.\overline{3}$_____ 5. $\dfrac{15 - 16 \div 4}{3 \cdot (45 - 2 \cdot 17)}$

_____5_____ 6. $120 \div 5 \div 4 - 1$

_____1,677_____ 7. $\dfrac{43 \cdot 15}{5} \cdot \dfrac{91}{7}$

_____28_____ 8. $14 + 29 - 5 - 21 + 11$

_____3_____ 9. $2{,}187 \div 3^3 \div 3^2 \div 3$

_____64_____ 10. $1{,}024 \div 2 \div 2 \div 2 \div 2$

_____−291_____ 11. $3 \times 568 - 228 \div 4 \times 35$

_____−13_____ 12. $364 \div 13 \div 7 - 51 \div 3$

_____−40_____ 13. $12 \times 4 \div 3 - 16 \div 2 \times 7$

_____7_____ 14. $(96 - 36) \div 12 + (156 - 86) \div 35$

_____1.5_____ 15. $(53 - 24 \div 3) \div (22 + 56 \div 7)$

_____−66_____ 16. $\sqrt{192 \div 12} - 140 \cdot \dfrac{1}{2}$

_____15_____ 17. $(15 \times 16 \div 12) - 35 \div 7$

_____0_____ 18. $3^8 \div 3^5 \div 9 - 3$

Problem Solving—Select the Operation (Use after 2.6.)

Use the following information to answer exercises 1–6.

A new Atlanta office tower with 27 floors is nearing completion. Except for the large retail business on the first floor, the number of offices per floor varies slightly due to each renter's space requirements. However, the average is about 40 offices per floor. Twenty percent of each floor's area is used for hallways, elevators, restrooms, and mechanical equipment needs. The building measures 140 ft. × 140 ft. and is 324 ft. tall.

_____1,040_____ 1. How many offices will be in the building?

_____2,106_____ 2. How many office desks will be in the building if each office has two desks and each office floor has a receptionist desk?

_____4,186_____ 3. How many chairs will be in the building if each desk has a chair and each office has two additional side chairs?

_____12 ft._____ 4. Assuming a consistent height for all floors, what is the height of each floor of the building?

_____3,920 ft.²_____ 5. How many square feet of each floor is dedicated to nonoffice space?

_____5,824_____ 6. The building looks like a large glass box because it has glass curtain walls. Each piece of glass is 5 ft. wide and 6 ft. high and is attached to a boxed aluminum frame that is visible on the inside but not on the outside. Excluding the first floor, how many pieces of glass will the 26 office floors require?

Use the election results given in the table to answer exercises 7–12.

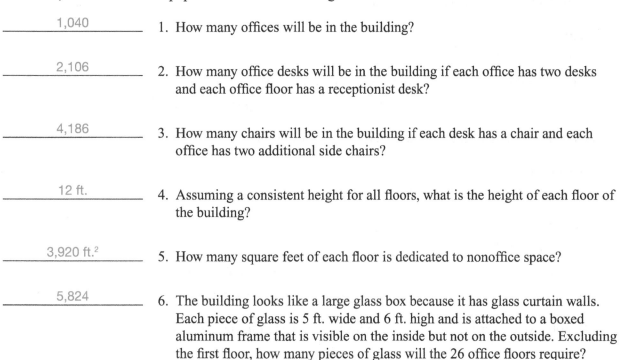

	District 1	District 2	District 3
Battaglia	4,298	3,629	5,268
McCloud	3,923	3,962	4,292
Garcia	5,240	3,727	2,927

_____13,195_____ 7. How many votes did Battaglia receive?

_____12,177_____ 8. How many votes did McCloud receive?

_____11,894_____ 9. How many votes did Garcia receive?

_____13,461_____ 10. How many voters were from District 1?

_____37,266_____ 11. How many people voted?

_____District 2_____ 12. Which district had the fewest number of voters?

Left-to-Right Mental Arithmetic (Enrichment; use after 2.7.)

Usually the basic operations of addition, subtraction, and multiplication are done right-to-left. But sometimes it is easier to add, subtract, or multiply mentally using a left-to-right method. When adding 588 + 217, you could use the following process.

Example 1

Find 588 + 217 by the left-to-right method.

Answer

$500 + 200 = 700$

$80 + 10 = 90$ The sum so far is $700 + 90 = 790$.

$8 + 7 = 15$ The final sum is $790 + 15 = 805$.

Subtraction and multiplication can also be done with this method.

Example 2

Find 6×381 by the left-to-right method.

Answer

$6 \times 300 = 1,800$

$6 \times 80 = 480$ The product so far is $1,800 + 480 = 2,280$.

$6 \times 1 = 6$ The final product is $2,280 + 6 = 2,286$.

The Distributive Property could also be combined with the left-to-right method.

$6(300 + 80 + 1) = 6(300) + 6(80) + 6(1) = 1,800 + 480 + 6 = 2,280 + 6 = 2,286$

Perform the indicated operations mentally using the left-to-right method.

_____1,005_____   1. $492 + 513$ _____414_____   2. $839 - 425$

_____295_____   3. $5 \cdot 59$ _____181_____   4. $672 - 491$

_____5,220_____   5. $4,902 + 318$ _____3,696_____   6. $7 \cdot 528$

_____1,241_____   7. $804 + 437$ _____1,551_____   8. $1,936 - 385$

_____3,870_____   9. $2 \cdot 1,935$ _____4,326_____   10. $6 \cdot 721$

Chapter 2 Review

Write T for true or F for false. If the statement is false, correct it.

_____T_____ 1. To evaluate an expression means to find its numerical value.

_____T_____ 2. Properties of addition are used in the computation and simplification of expressions.

_____F_____ 3. The Commutative Property states that the order in which numbers are multiplied or divided
will not change the answer.
The Commutative Property states that the order in which numbers are added or multiplied
will not change the answer.

_____F_____ 4. The Associative Property of Subtraction allows us to subtract three numbers in any order.
The Associative Property of Addition allows us to add three numbers in any order.

_____T_____ 5. Like terms in an expression can be combined into a single term.

_____F_____ 6. The Distributive Property still holds true if the multiplication sign is replaced with a
division sign.
The Distributive Property does not hold true if the multiplication sign is replaced with a
division sign. For example, $24 \div (8 + 4) = 24 \div 12 = 2$, but $24 \div 8 + 24 \div 4 = 3 + 6 = 9$.

_____T_____ 7. The Zero Property of Multiplication uses the identity element of addition.

Identify which property (Associative, Commutative, Distributive, Identity, or Inverse) is used to go from the left to the right side of each equation. Distinguish an addition property from a multiplication property.

8. $(8 + 14) + 0 = 8 + 14$
Identity Property of Addition

9. $-10 + (3 - 14) = (-10 + 3) - 14$
Associative Property of Addition

10. $5 \cdot 11 + 5 \cdot (-4) = 5(11 - 4)$
Distributive Property

11. $8(12 \cdot 3) = (8 \cdot 12)3$
Associative Property of Multiplication

12. $(7 + 9) + 11 = (9 + 7) + 11$
Commutative Property of Addition

13. $(x + 3)(2x - 7) + 9 = (2x - 7)(x + 3) + 9$
Commutative Property of Multiplication

14. $[8 + (-8)] + w = 0 + w$
Inverse Property of Addition

15. $-12 \cdot (21 \cdot 1) = -12 \cdot 21$
Identity Property of Multiplication

Simplify.

_____ $6x + 8$ _____ 16. $15x - 9x + 8$

_____ $-5y - 19$ _____ 17. $-16y + (11y - 19)$

_____ $378a^2b$ _____ 18. $9a(-7b)(2a)(-3)$

_____ $-90r$ _____ 19. $12r(-7) - (-7 + 13)r$

_____ $-4x^3$ _____ 20. $4x^3 - (2x)^3$

_____ 1 _____ 21. $[(3w) - (-8 + 19)w]^0$

Evaluate.

_____ -12 _____ 22. $6z - 36$ when $z = 4$

_____ 2 _____ 23. $\dfrac{12b + 2}{-11}$ when $b = -2$

_____ 148 _____ 24. $3^n + n^3 + 3$ when $n = 4$

_____ 810 _____ 25. $\dfrac{4r}{3} \times 15 - 150$ when $r = 48$

_____ -15 _____ 26. $5x - [21 - (3 - 11)x]$ when $x = -2$

_____ 12 _____ 27. $\dfrac{14x + 24 - 2x}{x + 2}$ when $x = -4$

_____ -88 _____ 28. $-4(x^2 + 4x + 1)$ when $x = 3$

_____ 4 _____ 29. $\dfrac{2x^2 + 5x + 12}{9 - 2x}$ when $x = -8$

_____ -410 _____ 30. $4x + 12xy - 5y$ when $x = -5$ and $y = 6$

_____ 3 _____ 31. $\dfrac{2a + 5b}{3x + 4y} + \dfrac{2a - b}{3x} - \dfrac{3ab}{2xy}$ when $a = -2$, $b = 8$, $x = -4$, and $y = 6$

Simplify each expression using the properties of addition or multiplication. Then evaluate each expression when $a = -2$, $b = 8$, $c = 3$, $x = -4$, and $y = 6$.

_____22_____ 32. $(a + 18) - (b - 14)$

_____133_____ 33. $5(a + 2b + 3c) - 9a$

_____20_____ 34. $3(x - y) + 5(2x + 3y)$

_____−72_____ 35. $4x - 3y + 2x - 5y$

_____153_____ 36. $9(2y) + (-21 + 11y)$

_____−2_____ 37. $\dfrac{x - 16 + 3x}{2y + 4}$

_____−2_____ 38. $\dfrac{2b - 4 + b}{5a}$

_____45_____ 39. $2a + 3b + 4c - 5a - 3(b - 3c)$

_____−34_____ 40. $ab + cx - y$

Write each word phrase as an algebraic expression.

_____$8n$_____ 41. the product of a number and 8

_____$n - 12$_____ 42. 12 less than a number

_____$-92 - n$_____ 43. −92 decreased by a number

_____$\dfrac{n}{5} + 7$_____ 44. 7 more than the quotient of a number and 5

_____$14 - x$_____ 45. Amy's age x years ago if she is 14 years old now

Estimate by rounding.

_____500_____ 46. $183 + 289$

_____600_____ 47. $5{,}226 \div 9$

_____100_____ 48. $725 - 595$

_____10_____ 49. $\dfrac{4{,}687}{496}$

_____1,500_____ 50. $932 + 315 + 258$

Cumulative Review 2

<u>b</u> 1. Identify the property used: $-8 + (6 - 3) = (6 - 3) - 8$.
   a. Associative
   b. Commutative
   c. Identity
   d. Inverse
   e. none of these

<u>c</u> 2. Identify the property used: $-5 \cdot (9 + 2) = (-5 \cdot 9) + (-5 \cdot 2)$.
   a. Associative
   b. Commutative
   c. Distributive
   d. Inverse
   e. none of these

<u>d</u> 3. Identify the property used: $(8x - 8x) + 3z = 0 + 3z$.
   a. Associative
   b. Commutative
   c. Distributive
   d. Inverse
   e. none of these

<u>d</u> 4. Simplify $8(3x) - 12(-7x) + 4(-9x)$.
   a. $-96x$
   b. $144x$
   c. $108x$
   d. $72x$
   e. none of these

<u>a</u> 5. Simplify $45 - 15 + (-6) + 16 + 2(-3)$.
   a. 34
   b. 46
   c. 58
   d. -27
   e. none of these

<u>b</u> 6. Simplify $|7 - 23| - |-16 + 2|$.
   a. 30
   b. 2
   c. 12
   d. 48
   e. none of these

<u>b</u> 7. Simplify and leave the answer in exponential form: $\frac{5 \cdot 5 \cdot 5 \cdot 5}{5}$.
   a. 5^5
   b. 5^3
   c. 5^4
   d. 5^2
   e. none of these

<u>d</u> 8. Simplify $w^5 \div w^9$.
   a. w^5
   b. w^9
   c. w^4
   d. $\frac{1}{w^4}$
   e. none of these

_____d_____ 9. Simplify $48 \div 4 \times 7 \div 3 - (12 - 7) \times 3 + 16$.
   a. −3   d. 29
   b. 85   e. none of these
   c. 13

_____c_____ 10. Write 4,680,000 in scientific notation.
   a. 4.68×10^{-3} d. 468.0×10^3
   b. 468.0×10^{-3} e. none of these
   c. 4.68×10^6

_____e_____ 11. Write 9.32×10^{-4} in standard form.
   a. 93.2   d. 0.00932
   b. 0.0932   e. none of these
   c. 9,320

_____b_____ 12. Evaluate $\dfrac{2x^2 - 6x + 9}{z^3 + 1}$ when $x = -4$ and $z = 4$.
   a. −1   d. $-\dfrac{1}{3}$
   b. 1   e. none of these
   c. $-\dfrac{1}{7}$

_____c_____ 13. Simplify by combining like terms: $4(2p - 3r + 12) - 5(p + r + 11)$.
   a. $3p - 7r - 7$ d. $3p - 7r + 7$
   b. $3p - 17r + 103$ e. none of these
   c. $3p - 17r - 7$

_____b_____ 14. Evaluate $5(a + 2b + 14) - 4b - 30$ when $a = -3$ and $b = 4$.
   a. 81   d. −49
   b. 49   e. none of these
   c. 158

_____d_____ 15. Alexa's car is four years old. It is twice as old as Eric's car. How old is Eric's car?
   a. 5 yr.   d. 2 yr.
   b. 4 yr.   e. none of these
   c. 3 yr.

3 Basic Equations and Inequalities

Creation Wonders—Earth (Bible Activity; use after 3.1.)

The Scriptures contain more than three hundred references to astronomical objects such as the sun, moon, and stars. We are encouraged to stand in awe and wonder of all God's handiwork. We live on a human-friendly planet filled with the beautiful and awesome works of our Creator. In Job 26:7–8 we read, "He stretcheth out the north over the empty place, and hangeth the earth upon nothing. He bindeth up the waters in his thick clouds; and the cloud is not rent under them."

God in infinite wisdom hung the earth on nothing by setting it and the other planets in orbit around the sun. The entire solar system operates as a balanced system of gravitational forces, like a big clock humming along year after year. When viewed from above the North Pole, the earth moves around the sun counterclockwise in an elliptical (oval), but almost circular, orbit. It is turning counterclockwise on its axis, and the moon is orbiting the earth counterclockwise in an elliptical path. The earth is at an ideal distance from the sun so that the water on the earth is mostly liquid. Clouds consist of tiny droplets suspended in air. If they were simply water vapor (gas), you would not be able to see them.

1. The average distance from the sun to Earth is 92,900,000 mi., which is denoted as 1 astronomical unit (AU). If the orbit of Saturn is 9.5 AU from the sun, what is the shortest possible distance from Earth to Saturn?
   789,650,000 mi.

2. If you were traveling at the speed of the *New Horizons* space probe, about 47,000 mi./hr., it would take you 56,000 yr. to reach the star nearest to our solar system. How long would it take to travel from Earth to Saturn? What does this tell you about the relative size of our solar system compared to the universe?
   700 days, or 1 month less than 2 yr.; Our solar system is a tiny speck in the vast universe.

In Genesis 8:22 the Lord promised, "While the earth remaineth, seedtime and harvest, and cold and heat, and summer and winter, and day and night shall not cease." The earth's rotation once every twenty-four hours gives us day and night. The other parts of the promise involve the change in seasons, which depends on a fascinating physical phenomenon of the earth.

3. Research and find what causes the change in the earth's seasons.
   The earth is tilted on its axis 23.5°.

Acts 14:17 states that both the fruitful seasons and the rain are gifts, proofs of God's goodness to humans. Psalm 147:8 describes God as the One "who covereth the heaven with clouds, who prepareth rain for the earth, who maketh grass to grow upon the mountains."

4. How many gallons of water would be dropped by a cloud if one inch of rain covered an area of one square mile? One cubic foot holds about 7.48 gal. of water. (Hint: All linear measures must be in the same unit. Therefore, change everything to feet.)
   17,377,536 gal.

Thy faithfulness is unto all generations: thou hast established the earth, and it abideth.
Psalm 119:90

Problem Solving—Guess and Check (Use after 3.2.)

For each problem, use the "guess and check" strategy to find the answer.

1. The product of two consecutive integers is 4,290. What are the integers?
   65, 66

2. The product of two consecutive prime numbers is 8,633. What are the prime numbers? ("Consecutive prime numbers" means there are no other prime numbers between them.)
   89, 97

3. Find the two integers between 1 and 1,000 that are both perfect squares and perfect cubes. What numbers to the sixth power would equal each of these amounts?
   $64 = 8^2 = 4^3$; $729 = 27^2 = 9^3$; $64 = 2^6$; $729 = 3^6$

4. Based on the structure of your answer to exercise 3, what is the next number that is both a perfect square and a perfect cube?
   $4,096 = 64^2 = 16^3 = 4^6$

5. Forty-one contestants are gathered for a competition involving bicycles (two wheels) and go-carts (four wheels). If there are 114 wheels in the staging area before the competition, how many bikes and how many go-carts are in the competition?
   25 bikes and 16 go-carts

6. Paula purchased almonds, walnuts, and cashews to make a large bowl of mixed nuts. She purchased almonds for $4.15/lb., walnuts for $4.95/lb., and cashews for $3.50/lb. If her total cost before taxes was $36.35, how many pounds of each did she purchase? (Assume that she purchased the nuts only in whole numbers of pounds.)
   almonds: 3 lb., walnuts: 2 lb., and cashews: 4 lb.

7. Omar had $0.83 in his pocket made up of just seven coins. What were the coins?
   3 pennies, 1 nickel, and 3 quarters

8. Construct an addition problem using seven 8s whose sum is exactly 200.
   $88 + 88 + 8 + 8 + 8 = 200$

9. Arrange three 7s using basic operations so that the value is 6.
   $7 - \frac{7}{7} = 6$

10. The value in each big circle is the sum of the digits in the adjacent small circles. What numbers would be placed in the small circles?

    a.
    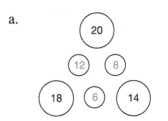

    b.
    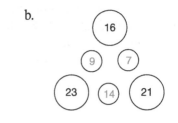

Lattice Squares (Enrichment; use after 3.2.)

Lattice squares are also called *fascinating squares* or *magic squares*. Even though there is nothing magic about magic squares, they are fun to construct. The numbers are placed in a 3 × 3 grid with the following rules:

1. Each number can be used only once.

2. All rows, columns, and main diagonals must have the same sum.

Example 1
Place the numbers 1–9 in the grid so that the sum of each row, column, and main diagonal is 15.

Answer

4	3	8
9	5	1
2	7	6

Check the sum of the rows: 4 + 3 + 8 = 15; 9 + 5 + 1 = 15; 2 + 7 + 6 = 15.

Check the sum of the columns: 4 + 9 + 2 = 15; 3 + 5 + 7 = 15; 8 + 1 + 6 = 15.

Check the sum of the main diagonals: 4 + 5 + 6 = 15; 2 + 5 + 8 = 15.

Find the missing numbers in the lattice squares. The sum of all rows, columns, and main diagonals must be 15.

1.

8	1	6
3	5	7
4	9	2

2.

8	3	4
1	5	9
6	7	2

3.

2	9	4
7	5	3
6	1	8

Are the following grids lattice squares? If yes, what is the common sum of each row, column, and main diagonal?

4. _____yes; 3_____

7	−7	3
−3	1	5
−1	9	−5

5. _____yes; 21_____

13	−1	9
3	7	11
5	15	1

6. _____yes; −15_____

−2	−9	−4
−7	−5	−3
−6	−1	−8

7. How does the sum relate to the center number in each of these lattice squares?
It is three times the center number.

8. Are these lattice squares made with consecutive numbers?
no, except for exercise 6

Lattice squares can be constructed using any set of consecutive integers. Use the patterns of the squares in exercises 1–3 and the list of numbers given to fill in the squares below. What is the sum of each row, column, and main diagonal?

9. Use the numbers 5–13. 27

12	5	10
7	9	11
8	13	6

10. Use the numbers 20–28. 72

27	22	23
20	24	28
25	26	21

11. Use the numbers 10–18. 42

11	18	13
16	14	12
15	10	17

Lattice squares can be constructed that start with three numbers a, b, and c such that $a > (b + c)$ and $2b \neq c$. The pattern is given below.

$a - b$	$a + b - c$	$a + c$
$a + b + c$	a	$a - b - c$
$a - c$	$a - b + c$	$a + b$

Example 2

Apply the pattern in the table above to create a lattice square. Let $a = 9$, $b = 3$, and $c = 2$. What is the sum of each row, column, and main diagonal?

Answer

$9 - 3$	$9 + 3 - 2$	$9 + 2$
$9 + 3 + 2$	9	$9 - 3 - 2$
$9 - 2$	$9 - 3 + 2$	$9 + 3$

6	10	11
14	9	4
7	8	12

The sum of each row, column, and main diagonal is 27.

Using the pattern above, construct lattice squares with the given values of a, b, and c. What is the sum of each row, column, and main diagonal?

12. $a = 15$, $b = 9$, $c = 4$ 45

6	20	19
28	15	2
11	10	24

13. $a = 30$, $b = 20$, $c = 5$ 90

10	45	35
55	30	5
25	15	50

14. $a = 6$, $b = -1$, $c = -4$ 18

7	9	2
1	6	11
10	3	5

Use the given lattice squares and the pattern above to determine the values of a, b, and c.

15. ___$a = 7$, $b = 3$, $c = 1$___

4	9	8
11	7	3
6	5	10

16. ___$a = 10$, $b = 3$, $c = 1$___

7	12	11
14	10	6
9	8	13

17. ___$a = 4$, $b = -2$, $c = 3$___

6	−1	7
5	4	3
1	9	2

18. Using the form of the pattern previous to Example 2, find the general value for the sum of each row, column, and main diagonal.

$3a$

Equations: Working Backwards (Enhanced Practice; use after 3.3.)

Working backwards can enable you to discover an unknown value. In an equation such as $3x + 5 = 32$, start with the result of 32 and work backwards using inverse operations to discover the unknown number x.

Example

A number is multiplied by 4. Then 9 is added. The result is 21. Find the unknown number.

Answer

Write the problem in equation form: $4x + 9 = 21$.

Work backwards: Start by subtracting 9 from 21, getting 12. Then divide by 4, getting 3. The unknown number is 3.

Check your answer: $4(3) = 12$; $12 + 9 = 21$; 21 is the correct number, so 3 is the correct answer.

Write an equation for each problem and work backwards to find the unknown number. Check your answer.

1. Unknown number → divide by 5 → subtract 9 → result is 1.

$\frac{x}{5} - 9 = 1$; $x = 50$

2. Unknown number → add 4 → multiply by 5 → result is 55.

$5(x + 4) = 55$; $x = 7$

3. Unknown number → multiply by 3 → subtract 4 → divide by 2 → result is 16.

$\frac{3x - 4}{2} = 16$; $x = 12$

4. Unknown number → multiply by $\frac{1}{2}$ → add 8 → result is 5.

$\frac{1}{2}x + 8 = 5$; $x = -6$

Solve each equation by working backwards. Show all of your work.

_____−3_____ 5. $2a + 9 = 3$

_____12_____ 6. $\frac{f}{2} - 4 = 2$

_____3_____ 7. $5c - 7 = 8$

_____−18_____ 8. $\frac{1}{9}d + 7 = 5$

_____−4_____ 9. $7e + 11 = -17$

_____−42_____ 10. $\frac{f}{3} - 8 = -22$

Simplifying Before Solving (Extra Practice; use after 3.4.)

Solve for the variable.

_____3_____ 1. $4a + 7a - 4 = 29$

_____−2_____ 2. $6b - 9 - 2b = -17$

_____−4_____ 3. $4(c + 5) - 2c = 12$

_____3_____ 4. $3(4d) - 8 - 2d = 22$

_____3_____ 5. $6p + 2 + 3p - p = 26$

_____1_____ 6. $3(k - 5) + 9 - k = -4$

_____−8_____ 7. $2(w + 3) - 8 = -18$

_____−14_____ 8. $14 + 2(z - 1) = -16$

_____7_____ 9. $-5 \cdot 12d + 64 = -356$

_____−5_____ 10. $z + 5 + 2(z + 6) = 2$

_____32_____ 11. $132 - 2(2b - 3) + 1 = 11$

_____2_____ 12. $2(w - 1) + 3(w - 2) = 2$

_____−4_____ 13. $3(x + 9) - x = 19$

_____−28_____ 14. $3x - 4(x + 5) = 8$

_____132_____ 15. $\dfrac{2y + 4 - 3y}{16} = -8$

_____2_____ 16. $\dfrac{5k + 8}{6} = 3$

_____13_____ 17. $\dfrac{4(x - 1)}{6} = 8$

_____10_____ 18. $\dfrac{5(x + 8)}{9} = 10$

_____22_____ 19. $\frac{1}{4}(x + 6) = 7$

_____−6_____ 20. $9 + \dfrac{4c}{-3} = 17$

Calculator Skill 3 <small>(Use after 3.5.)</small>

written for the TI-30Xa

The exercise sets in math textbooks typically have equations containing integers or simple fractions. However, in the context of real-life application problems, numbers are often larger and may include several decimal places. A calculator helps you in solving such applications so that you don't have to manipulate cumbersome arithmetic problems. Tedious arithmetic can sometimes take the thrill out of solving interesting and useful problems.

Example 1

Solve the equation $8.325x = 18.315$ for x.

Answer

Divide by the coefficient of x: $\frac{8.325x}{8.325} = \frac{18.315}{8.325}$. The result is $x = 2.2$.

Example 2

If 25 out of every 300 men are known to have some color perception deficiency, then how many men attended a seminar where 64 of them performed less than perfect on a color perception test?

Answer

Let x = the number of attendees.

Write a proportion using ratios to compare the number of people with deficiencies to the total number of people: $\frac{25}{300} = \frac{64}{x}$.

Use cross multiplication to obtain the equation $25x = 300(64)$.

$25x = 19,200$

$\frac{25x}{25} = \frac{19,200}{25}$

$x = 768$ attendees

Determine whether the value given for x is a solution to the equation.

__yes__   1. $6.45x = 33.153; x = 5.14$

__no__   2. $0.0025x = 0.000035; x = 0.0014$

__yes__   3. $18,340x = 10,178.7; x = 0.555$

__no__   4. $\frac{x}{385.5} = 6,329.91; x = 16.42$

__no__   5. $14,986 = 70x; x = 214$

Solve for the variable. Round answers to the nearest thousandth if necessary.

_____0.205_____ 6. $180.55x = 37.01275$

_____125.75_____ 7. $2{,}577.875 = 20.5x$

_____7.6_____ 8. $375x = 2{,}850$

_____−17.659_____ 9. $\frac{21}{56}x = -6\frac{28}{45}$

_____4.326_____ 10. $10.21 = 2.36x$

Write an equation and solve.

11. The bronze alloy used for bells is typically 78% copper and 22% tin. How much copper is in a bronze bell weighing 2,080 lb.?

   $x = 0.78(2{,}080)$; 1,622.4 lb.

12. Each of the twin booster rockets on a launch vehicle burns solid fuel at a rate of 18,333 lb./sec. If together the rockets contain 2.2 million lb. of solid fuel, how many minutes will each one burn during a launch?

   $18{,}333x = 1{,}100{,}000$; about 1 min.

13. Anna bought a new sweater for $25 during a 20% off sale. What was the original price of the sweater?

   $0.8x = 25$; \$31.25

14. If a racecar traveling at top speed around a 2 mi. oval track takes 32 sec. per lap, how many miles per second is the racecar traveling? Convert this figure to miles per hour.

   $d = rt$; $2 = 32r$; $r = 0.0625$ mi./sec. = 225 mi./hr.

15. At the end of the last quarter Mr. Roberts had investments in the stock market worth $242,245. His most recent quarterly investment report shows that his investments are now worth $246,450. If he made no additional deposits, how many dollars of growth did he experience?

   $242{,}245 + x = 246{,}450$; \$4,205 of growth

Chapter 3 Review

Write T for true or F for false. If the statement is false, correct it.

_____F_____ 1. The Multiplication Property of Equality guarantees that $x + 6 = 19$ gives $x = 13$.
The Addition Property of Equality is used to solve this equation.

_____F_____ 2. The Addition Property of Equality guarantees that $3b = 27$ gives $b = 9$.
The Multiplication Property of Equality is used to solve this equation.

_____T_____ 3. The equation $5a = 3(a + 4)$ becomes $5a = 3a + 12$ by the Distributive Property.

_____T_____ 4. $\frac{1}{3}(n - 8) = 24$ is the translated form of "one-third of the difference between a number and 8 is 24."

_____F_____ 5. $n + \frac{1}{10}n = 2{,}200$ is the translated form of "Mr. Cable's salary, denoted as n, minus one-tenth of his salary for his tithe, is $2,200."
The plus sign should be a minus sign.

_____F_____ 6. $x + 2x = 460$ is the translated form of "The Real Sports Shop has twice as many men's golf clubs as women's among the 460 clubs in stock. There are x number of men's clubs."
The variable should represent the number of women's clubs or the equation should be rewritten.

Write an equation using x for the variable for each sentence below. Do not solve.

$\frac{1}{10}(3{,}500) = x + 250$
_____ 7. One-tenth of the 3,500 mortgages is 250 more than the number of delinquent mortgages.

$4x = 3x + 40$
_____ 8. Four times a number is 40 more than three times the number.

$2x + 16 = 838$
_____ 9. Danielle has 838 stamps in her collection, which is 16 more than twice as many as her brother Darien has.

Solve for the variable.

_____−7_____ 10. $5w + 9 - 2w = -12$

_____2_____ 11. $6(3d + 2) - 8 = 40$

_____−10_____ 12. $\dfrac{2x - 16}{-2} = 18$

_____9_____ 13. $2(z - 4) + 2 - 6z = -42$

_____4_____ 14. $-8(5b) + 94 + 4b = -50$

_____−99_____ 15. $\dfrac{5(x + 3) - 4x}{4} = -21$

Solve the following inequalities.

_____$a < 11$_____ 16. $2a + 5 < 27$

_____$y \geq -5$_____ 17. $12y - 2y \geq -50$

_____$d \geq 10$_____ 18. $-4d + 18 \leq -22$

_____$c \neq 4$_____ 19. $11(c - 4) - 10c \neq -40$

_____$w > 5$_____ 20. $3w + 2(w - 11) > 3$

_____$x > 3$_____ 21. $7x + 42 - 11x < 30$

_____$p \geq -6$_____ 22. $\dfrac{4(p - 9)}{12} \geq -5$

_____$z \geq -15$_____ 23. $-6(3z + 1) - 8 + 15z \leq 31$

Write an equation and solve.

24. Zizi bought four bottles of soft drink at $1 each and several cans of mixed nuts at $4 each. If the bill was $20, how many cans of nuts did she purchase? (Ignore sales tax.)
$4x + 4(1) = 20$; 4 cans

25. The Celinski family traveled 1,890 mi. on their vacation and used 84 gal. of gasoline. What was their vehicle's gas mileage (mi./gal.)? (Hint: gallons × gas mileage = distance.)
$84x = 1,890$; 22.5 mi./gal.

26. Jillian needs 3 yd. of material to make a bag for each child in her Bible club. If she has 39 yd. of material, how many bags can she make?
$3x = 39$; 13 bags

27. A jet travels 2,528 mi. in 4 hr. What is the average speed of the jet?
$4x = 2,528$; 632 mi./hr.

Place the given numbers in the correct set on the Venn diagram.

28. 52

29. $\frac{1}{2}$

30. -6

31. $-\frac{3}{7}$

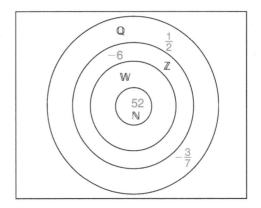

Which numbers are members of the solution sets for the given inequalities?

<u>   1, 2   </u>   32. $x + 7 \geq 8$; $-1, 0, 1, 2$

<u>   2, 4   </u>   33. $-6x < 48$; $-9, -8, 2, 4$

<u> $-3, -2, 0, 1$ </u>   34. $y + 8 \neq 7$; $-3, -2, -1, 0, 1$

<u>   203   </u>   35. $51 > \frac{z}{4}$; $203, 204, 205$

Write an inequality, solve it, and express the answer in words.

36. Dixie sold six puppies and made more than $900 from the sales. How much did she receive for each puppy?

$6p > 900$; $p > 150$; Each puppy cost more than $150.

37. James has $50 to spend on baseballs for his team. If each baseball costs $4, what is the maximum number that he can buy?

$4x \leq 50$; $x \leq 12.5$; James can buy a maximum of 12 baseballs.

Cumulative Review 3

_____a_____ 1. Simplify $|-8 + (-5)| - |16 + (-7) - 1|$.
- a. 5
- b. 21
- c. −11
- d. −5
- e. none of these

_____d_____ 2. Simplify $-120 \div 15 \times (-4)$.
- a. −2
- b. 2
- c. −32
- d. 32
- e. none of these

_____b_____ 3. Simplify $\dfrac{5(-13) + 2}{-7} \cdot 3$.
- a. −27
- b. 27
- c. 9
- d. 7.44
- e. none of these

_____e_____ 4. Simplify $-2^4 + 4^2$.
- a. 32
- b. −32
- c. 16
- d. −16
- e. none of these

_____c_____ 5. Write 0.00000000024 in scientific notation.
- a. 24×10^9
- b. 2.4×10^{10}
- c. 2.4×10^{-10}
- d. 24×10^{-9}
- e. none of these

_____c_____ 6. Identify the property used: $[2 + (-5)] + 7 = 2 + (-5 + 7)$.
- a. Closure Property
- b. Commutative Property
- c. Associative Property
- d. Distributive Property
- e. none of these

_____a_____ 7. Which of the following sets are closed under multiplication?
- a. $\{1, 3, 6, \ldots\}$
- b. $\{0, 5, 10, 15\}$
- c. $\{2, 4, 6, 8\}$
- d. $\{0, 1, 2\}$
- e. none of these

_____b_____ 8. Identify the property used: $x(z^3 \cdot y^4) = (z^3 \cdot y^4)x$.
- a. Closure Property
- b. Commutative Property
- c. Associative Property
- d. Distributive Property
- e. none of these

_____d_____ 9. Use the Distributive Property to find the value of the variable: $(b + 8)4 = 3 \cdot 4 + 8 \cdot 4$.
   - a. $b = 4$
   - b. $b = -4$
   - c. $b = -3$
   - d. $b = 3$
   - e. none of these

_____b_____ 10. Use the Distributive Property to simplify $4(x + 6)$.
   - a. $4x + 6$
   - b. $4x + 24$
   - c. $x + 24$
   - d. $4x^2 + 6x$
   - e. none of these

_____c_____ 11. Use the Distributive Property to evaluate $-8(3 - 11)$.
   - a. 112
   - b. -112
   - c. 64
   - d. -64
   - e. none of these

_____a_____ 12. Evaluate $3a + b$ when $a = -3$ and $b = 8$.
   - a. -1
   - b. 1
   - c. -17
   - d. 17
   - e. none of these

_____d_____ 13. Evaluate $a + 2x - y + b$ when $a = 2$, $b = -5$, $x = 4$, and $y = -1$.
   - a. 2
   - b. 4
   - c. 14
   - d. 6
   - e. none of these

_____d_____ 14. Simplify $8p - 4q - 2p - 3q + 4$.
   - a. $4p - 5q$
   - b. $4p - 5q + 4$
   - c. $6p - q + 4$
   - d. $6p - 7q + 4$
   - e. none of these

_____b_____ 15. Simplify $\frac{48x^3}{6x^2}$.
   - a. $8x^5$
   - b. $8x$
   - c. $8x^2$
   - d. $8x^{-2}$
   - e. none of these

4 Number Theory

Prime and Composite Numbers   (Enhanced Practice; use after 4.1.)

In order to decide whether a number is prime or composite, you must know whether there are any numbers besides one and itself that divide it. Divisibility tests are useful in checking for factors of a given number. It is also desirable to check as few factors as possible. The following theorem will reduce your work considerably.

Theorem: If a number n is composite, then n has a prime factor p such that $p^2 \le n$.

Example 1

Is 89 prime or composite?

Answer

Determine the largest prime number, p, such that $p^2 \le 89$.

$7^2 < 89$, but $11^2 > 89$.

Therefore, if a prime number is a factor of 89, it must be less than or equal to 7.

Check divisibility for 2, 3, 5, and 7. None of these prime numbers divide 89.

Therefore, 89 is prime.

Use the divisibility tests to label each number as prime (P) or composite (C).

_C_ 1. 46   _C_ 2. 57   _C_ 3. 63

_C_ 4. 72   _P_ 5. 79   _C_ 6. 93

_P_ 7. 101   _P_ 8. 113   _P_ 9. 127

_C_ 10. 183   _C_ 11. 221   _P_ 12. 281

Goldbach's Conjecture: The proof of the following statement made in 1742 by Russian mathematician Christian Goldbach, or the modern equivalent of that proof, is one of the oldest unsolved problems in mathematics.

Every even number larger than two can be written as the sum of two prime numbers.

While the presence of a counterexample disproves a statement, the lack of a counterexample is not sufficient to prove it. Although Goldbach's conjecture has been verified through 10^{18}, it still has not been proven.

Note that as the even numbers get larger, more pairs of primes can be used in the sum.

Example 2

Express the even numbers 6, 8, 10, and 16 as a sum of two prime numbers.

Answer

$6 = 3 + 3$; $8 = 3 + 5$; $10 = 3 + 7$ or $10 = 5 + 5$; $16 = 3 + 13$ or $16 = 5 + 11$

Express each of the given even numbers as the sum of two prime numbers. Answers may vary.

_____5 + 13, 7 + 11_____ 13. 18

_____5 + 19, 7 + 17, 11 + 13_____ 14. 24

_____7 + 31, 19 + 19_____ 15. 38

_____7 + 37, 13 + 31_____ 16. 44

___3 + 53, 13 + 43, 19 + 37___ 17. 56

___3 + 61, 5 + 59, 11 + 53, 17 + 47___ 18. 64

___7 + 73, 13 + 67, 19 + 61,___ 19. 80
___37 + 43___

___3 + 89, 13 + 79, 19 + 73___ 20. 92

___3 + 97, 11 + 89, 29 + 71___ 21. 100

___11 + 113, 17 + 107, 23 + 101___ 22. 124

Twin primes are two prime numbers that have a difference of 2. For example, 5 and 3 are twin primes.

23. List all twin primes between 2 and 100.
    3 and 5; 5 and 7; 11 and 13; 17 and 19; 29 and 31; 41 and 43; 59 and 61; 71 and 73

Find the pattern, give the next three numbers in the sequence, and explain how the sequence is formed.

24. 2, 3, 5, 7, 11, 13, …
    17, 19, 23; ascending primes

25. 97, 89, 83, …
    79, 73, 71; descending primes

26. 2, 5, 10, 17, 28, 41, …
    58, 77, 100; adding the next larger prime (3, 5, 7, etc.)

27. 2, 6, 30, 210, …
    2,310; 30,030; 510,510; multiplying by the next larger prime (3, 5, 7, etc.)

_____56_____ 28. What is the smallest number divisible by 8 and 14?

_____72_____ 29. What is the largest number less than 100 divisible by 4 and 18?

Make a Conjecture

30. What operation is not closed for the set of integers?
    division

31. Verify your answer to exercise 30 with a counterexample.
    Answers will vary. $2 \div 4 = 0.5$, which is not an integer.

Creation Wonders—The Flood (Bible Activity; use after 4.1.)

The Scriptures teach that Noah's Flood was a universal flood; that is, it covered all of the earth. Genesis 7:19 states, "and all the high hills, that were under the whole heaven, were covered." The Bible does not give a lot of information about the geology or topology of the earth before the Flood; but Genesis 2:5–6 does say that rather than rain, a mist from the earth watered the ground.

The Flood of Noah's day was designed and carried out by God as a means of judging mankind for their prevailing evil. This Flood was of such catastrophic proportions that vast changes took place in the earth's surface. The present condition of the earth, with the high mountains and the deep canyons of the oceans, easily accommodates the huge amount of water produced by the Flood. If one were to level the earth's surface by removing the mountains and continents and filling in the sea, the water that presently exists would cover the earth 1.7 mi. deep. As it is, water covers 70% of the earth and land covers 30%.

Even though the Scriptures speak clearly about Noah's ark and the extent of the Flood, these continue to be points of great controversy in our age and a favorite topic of the world's scoffers. Second Peter 3:5–6 reveals the true nature of these scoffers: "For this they willingly are ignorant of, that by the word of God the heavens were of old, and the earth standing out of the water and in the water: whereby the world that then was, being overflowed with water, perished."

1. Read Genesis 7. According to verse 11, where did all the water for the Flood come from?
   the fountains of the deep and the windows of heaven

If we find the rainfall intensity in inches per hour for forty days of rain, we can make some conclusions about the two sources of water in Genesis 7:11.

2. If the water on earth was 1.7 mi. deep and it took 40 days to obtain this amount of rainfall, what is the amount of rain that would have to fall per hour?
   about 112 in./hr.

3. Rains that accompany tropical storms have rainfall intensities of 6 to 8 in./hr. Is it more likely that most of the water during the Flood came from rainfall or from the fountains of the deep?
   The fountains of the deep must have provided most of the water.

4. Read Genesis 8 and find out how many days it was from the start of the rain until the ark rested on a mountain in the greater Ararat chain of mountains.
   150 days

5. How long did it take in days from the start of the rain until the tops of the mountains were visible? Assume an average of 30 days in a month.
   about 224 days

6. How many days were Noah and his family in the ark with the animals?
   about 382 days

7. What did Jesus teach about Noah and the Flood? Why is His teaching valuable information for this age of Flood-story scoffers?
   The condition of people when Christ returns will be like that of the people of Noah's day. Jesus, as God, confirmed the truth of Noah and the Flood (Matt. 24:37–39).

> *And I will establish my covenant with you; neither shall all flesh be cut off any more*
> *by the waters of a flood; neither shall there any more be a flood to destroy the earth.*
> Genesis 9:11

Perfect, Deficient, and Abundant Numbers (Enrichment; use after 4.2.)

The ancient Greeks enjoyed classifying numbers greater than one as *perfect*, *deficient*, or *abundant* based on the following criteria. (A proper factor is any factor other than the number itself.)

Perfect: the sum of a number's proper factors equals the number (e.g., $1 + 2 + 3 = 6$).

Deficient: the sum of a number's proper factors is less than the number (e.g., $1 + 2 + 4 = 7 < 8$).

Abundant: the sum of a number's proper factors is greater than the number
(e.g., $1 + 2 + 3 + 4 + 6 = 16 > 12$).

There are very few perfect numbers. In fact, there are only three of them less than 1,000. With the advent of highly sophisticated computers, the list of perfect numbers has expanded recently to 44. The ancient Greek mathematician Euclid developed a formula for finding perfect numbers in Book 9 of *The Elements*. He proved that if one knows that $2^n - 1$ is a prime number, then $(2^{n-1})(2^n - 1)$ is a perfect number.

List all the proper factors of each of the given numbers. Find the sum of the proper factors and identify each number as *perfect*, *deficient*, or *abundant*.

	Number	Factors	Sum of Factors	Type of Number
1.	4	1, 2	3	deficient
2.	9	1, 3	4	deficient
3.	16	1, 2, 4, 8	15	deficient
4.	18	1, 2, 3, 6, 9	21	abundant
5.	20	1, 2, 4, 5, 10	22	abundant
6.	22	1, 2, 11	14	deficient
7.	24	1, 2, 3, 4, 6, 8, 12	36	abundant
8.	28	1, 2, 4, 7, 14	28	perfect
9.	30	1, 2, 3, 5, 6, 10, 15	42	abundant
10.	32	1, 2, 4, 8, 16	31	deficient
11.	34	1, 2, 17	20	deficient
12.	36	1, 2, 3, 4, 6, 9, 12, 18	55	abundant
13.	40	1, 2, 4, 5, 8, 10, 20	50	abundant
14.	45	1, 3, 5, 9, 15	33	deficient
15.	47	1	1	deficient
16.	100	1, 2, 4, 5, 10, 20, 25, 50	117	abundant
17.	250	1, 2, 5, 10, 25, 50, 125	218	deficient
18.	496	1, 2, 4, 8, 16, 31, 62, 124, 248	496	perfect
19.	3,125	1, 5, 25, 125, 625	781	deficient
20.	8,128	1; 2; 4; 8; 16; 32; 64; 127; 254; 508; 1,016; 2,032; 4,064	8,128	perfect

GCF and LCM (Extra Practice; use after 4.4.)

Use either listing or prime factorizations to find the GCF of each pair of numbers.

_____2_____ 1. 8, 18 _____4_____ 2. 12, 32 _____3_____ 3. 15, 36

_____1_____ 4. 16, 33 _____3_____ 5. 9, 66 _____11_____ 6. 11, 165

_____6_____ 7. 24, 18 _____3_____ 8. 27, 39 _____15_____ 9. 30, 45

_____18_____ 10. 36, 54 _____19_____ 11. 38, 95 _____39_____ 12. 39, 78

_____4_____ 13. In which of exercises 1–12 was the pair of numbers *relatively prime*?

Use prime factorizations to find the GCF of each set of numbers.

_____21_____ 14. 42, 63 _____24_____ 15. 72, 120

_____36_____ 16. 108, 144 _____7_____ 17. 91, 105

_____3_____ 18. 12, 36, 45 _____3_____ 19. 15, 24, 39

_____16_____ 20. 16, 64, 96 _____2_____ 21. 24, 92, 138

_____4_____ 22. 12, 20, 28, 44 _____6_____ 23. 30, 48, 72, 90

_____13_____ 24. 39, 65, 91, 143 _____21_____ 25. 42, 105, 147

Find the GCF of these numbers given in factored form. Leave answers in factored form.

_____$2^2 \cdot 3^2 \cdot 5$_____ 26. $2^3 \cdot 3^2 \cdot 5$ and $2^2 \cdot 3^2 \cdot 5^2$

_____$2 \cdot 3 \cdot 5^2 \cdot 13$_____ 27. $2^3 \cdot 3 \cdot 5^2 \cdot 7^2 \cdot 13^2$ and $2 \cdot 3^2 \cdot 5^3 \cdot 13$

_____$2 \cdot 3 \cdot 5 \cdot 7$_____ 28. $2^3 \cdot 3 \cdot 5 \cdot 7$, $2 \cdot 3^2 \cdot 5^2 \cdot 7^2$, and $2^2 \cdot 3 \cdot 5 \cdot 7$

_____3_____ 29. $3 \cdot 5^2 \cdot 17$ and $2^2 \cdot 3^2 \cdot 13$

_____$3 \cdot 5$_____ 30. $3 \cdot 5^2 \cdot 7$ and $2^2 \cdot 3 \cdot 5 \cdot 11$

List multiples to find the LCM of each pair of numbers.

_____10_____ 31. 2, 5

_____63_____ 32. 7, 9

_____84_____ 33. 7, 12

_____40_____ 34. 5, 8

_____18_____ 35. 6, 9

_____50_____ 36. 10, 25

_____105_____ 37. 15, 35

_____60_____ 38. 6, 20

_____56_____ 39. 8, 14

Find the LCM of these numbers given in factored form. Leave answers in factored form.

_____$2^3 \cdot 3^2 \cdot 5^2$_____ 40. $2^3 \cdot 3^2 \cdot 5$ and $2^2 \cdot 3^2 \cdot 5^2$

_____$2^2 \cdot 3 \cdot 5^2 \cdot 7 \cdot 11$_____ 41. $3 \cdot 5^2 \cdot 7$ and $2^2 \cdot 3 \cdot 5 \cdot 11$

_____$2^3 \cdot 3^2 \cdot 5^3 \cdot 7^2 \cdot 13^2$_____ 42. $2^3 \cdot 3 \cdot 5^2 \cdot 7^2 \cdot 13^2$ and $2 \cdot 3^2 \cdot 5^3 \cdot 13$

_____$2^3 \cdot 3^2 \cdot 5^2 \cdot 7^2$_____ 43. $2^3 \cdot 3 \cdot 5 \cdot 7$, $2 \cdot 3^2 \cdot 5^2 \cdot 7^2$, and $2^2 \cdot 3 \cdot 5 \cdot 7$

Use prime factorizations to find the LCM of each set of numbers.

_____40_____ 44. 8, 20

_____60_____ 45. 12, 15

_____336_____ 46. 16, 21

_____180_____ 47. 36, 45

_____84_____ 48. 28, 42

_____72_____ 49. 8, 12, 18

_____1,188_____ 50. 12, 27, 33

_____252_____ 51. 18, 42, 84

_____864_____ 52. 27, 54, 96

_____9,576_____ 53. 36, 56, 76

_____14,784_____ 54. 44, 64, 84

_____216_____ 55. 8, 12, 18, 27

Calculator Skill 4 (Use after 4.4.)

written for the TI-30Xa

The Greatest Common Factor (GCF)

You have already learned how to use lists of factors or prime factorizations to find the GCF of two or more numbers, but there are two other methods that work well on a calculator.

The first method uses the *Division Algorithm* repeatedly. The Division Algorithm states that long division allows you to find a quotient and remainder. Study Example 1 carefully to see the steps involved. The permissibility of repeatedly using the Division Algorithm is proven in a theorem called the Euclidean Algorithm.

The second method is the reduced fraction method. Example 2 illustrates this method. It cannot be used with the TI-30Xa if the divisor has more than three digits.

Example 1

Find the GCF of 1,528 and 364 using the Division Algorithm.

Answer

Step 1: Use the larger number as the dividend and the smaller number as the divisor.

$1{,}528 \div 364 \approx 4.2$.

Subtract 4×364 from 1,528 to find the remainder, 72.

$1{,}528 = 4 \times 364 + 72$

Step 2: Then divide the divisor by the remainder. $364 \div 72 \approx 5.1$.

Subtract 5×72 from 364 to find the remainder, 4.

$364 = 5 \times 72 + 4$

Step 3: Again, divide the divisor by the remainder. $72 \div 4 = 18$ with no remainder.

$72 = 4 \times 18 + 0$

Continue the process until the remainder is zero. Since the remainder is 0 when you divide by 4, you can conclude that 4 divides 72. Therefore, 4 divides 364 and, in turn, 4 divides 1,528. The GCF of 1,528 and 364 is 4.

Example 2

Find the GCF of 832 and 312 using the reduced fraction method.

Answer

Enter the fraction $\frac{312}{832}$ using the keystrokes 312 $\boxed{A\frac{b}{c}}$ 832. Now press $\boxed{=}$ to reduce the fraction, giving $\frac{312}{832} = \frac{3}{8}$. Then divide the numerators: $312 \div 3 = 104$; and divide the denominators: $832 \div 8 = 104$. Since 104 is a factor of both 312 and 832, it is the GCF of 832 and 312.

The Least Common Multiple (LCM)

An interesting and very useful property relates the GCF to the LCM of two numbers. This property lets us find the LCM quickly once we know the GCF. The property says that the GCF times the LCM of two numbers equals the product of the two numbers.

$$\text{GCF}\,(a, b) \times \text{LCM}\,(a, b) = a \times b$$

Example 3

Find the LCM of 1,528 and 364 using the property above and the answer from Example 1.

Answer

$GCF\ (a, b) \times LCM\ (a, b) = a \times b$

$4 \times LCM\ (1{,}528;\ 364) = 1{,}528 \times 364$

$LCM\ (1{,}528;\ 364) = \dfrac{556{,}192}{4} = 139{,}048$

Example 4

Find the LCM of 832 and 312 using the property above and the answer from Example 2.

Answer

$104 \times LCM\ (832,\ 312) = 832 \times 312$

$LCM\ (832,\ 312) = \dfrac{259{,}584}{104} = 2{,}496$

Calculate the GCF of each pair of numbers using the Division Algorithm or the reduced fraction method. Then find the LCM of each pair.

<u>GCF = 37; LCM = 6,216</u>   1. 259, 888

<u>GCF = 5; LCM = 124,950</u>   2. 735, 850

<u>GCF = 4; LCM = 269,816</u>   3. 232; 4,652

<u>GCF = 5; LCM = 1,282,020</u>   4. 345; 18,580

<u>GCF = 1; LCM = 9,699,690</u>   5. 1,870; 5,187

<u>GCF = 4</u>   6. If the LCM of 824 and 1,692 is 348,552, find their GCF.

<u>b = 360</u>   7. If the GCF of 81 and b is 9 and their LCM is 3,240, find b.

<u>2,295</u>   8. Find the LCM of 85 and 135.

<u>35,160</u>   9. Find the LCM of 120 and 586.

10. Find all possible pairs of values for a and b such that GCF $(a, b) = 11$ and LCM $(a, b) = 132$.
    33 and 44; 22 and 66; 11 and 132

Arithmetic and Geometric Sequences   (Extra Practice; use after 4.6.)

Write the first five terms of the following recursively defined sequences.

_____4, 7, 10, 13, 16_____ 1. $a_1 = 4; a_n = a_{n-1} + 3$

_____5, 12, 19, 26, 33_____ 2. $a_1 = 5; a_n = a_{n-1} + 7$

_____−2, 2, 6, 10, 14_____ 3. $a_1 = -2; a_n = a_{n-1} + 4$

_____21, 13, 5, −3, −11_____ 4. $a_1 = 21; a_n = a_{n-1} - 8$

Write the first five terms of the following explicitly defined sequences.

_____−1, 2, 5, 8, 11_____ 5. $a_n = -1 + (n-1)3$

_____−7, −5, −3, −1, 1_____ 6. $a_n = -7 + (n-1)2$

_____8, 10, 12, 14, 16_____ 7. $a_n = 2n + 6$

_____4, 9, 14, 19, 24_____ 8. $a_n = 5n - 1$

Write the simplified form of the explicit formula for the following sequences; then find a_{50}.

_____$a_n = 4n - 3$; 197_____ 9. 1, 5, 9, 13, …

_____$a_n = -3n + 15$; −135_____ 10. 12, 9, 6, 3, …

_____$a_n = 4n - 9$; 191_____ 11. −5, −1, 3, 7, …

_____$a_n = -6n + 5$; −295_____ 12. −1, −7, −13, …

Write the next four terms of the following sequences.

_____3, 6, 9, 12_____ 13. −6, −3, 0, …

_____16, 21, 26, 31_____ 14. 1, 6, 11, …

_____23, 29, 35, 41_____ 15. 5, 11, 17, …

_____15, 24, 33, 42_____ 16. −12, −3, 6, …

Write the first five terms of the following recursively defined sequences.

_4, 8, 16, 32, 64_   17. $a_1 = 4$; $a_n = 2a_{n-1}$

_−2, −6, −18, −54, −162_   18. $a_1 = -2$; $a_n = 3a_{n-1}$

_2, −4, 8, −16, 32_   19. $a_1 = 2$; $a_n = -2a_{n-1}$

8, 4, 2, 1, $\frac{1}{2}$ 20. $a_1 = 8$; $a_n = \frac{1}{2}a_{n-1}$

Write the recursive definition for the following sequences.

_$a_1 = 3$; $a_n = 2a_{n-1}$_   21. 3, 6, 12, …

_$a_1 = 1$; $a_n = -3a_{n-1}$_   22. 1, −3, 9, −27, …

_$a_1 = 16$; $a_n = \frac{1}{2}a_{n-1}$_   23. 16, 8, 4, …

_$a_1 = 81$; $a_n = -\frac{1}{3}a_{n-1}$_   24. 81, −27, 9, −3, …

Write the explicit formula for the following sequences; then find a_{10}.

_$a_n = 2(3)^{n-1}$; 39,366_   25. 2, 6, 18, 54, …

_$a_n = 3(-2)^{n-1}$; −1,536_   26. 3, −6, 12, −24, …

_$a_n = 1,024\left(\frac{1}{2}\right)^{n-1}$; 2_   27. 1,024, 512, 256, 128, …

_$a_n = (-2)^{n-1}$; −512_   28. 1, −2, 4, −8, …

Write the next four terms of the following sequences.

_16, −32, 64, −128_   29. 1, −2, 4, −8, …

_48, 96, 192, 384_   30. 3, 6, 12, 24, …

_81, −243, 729, −2,187_   31. 1, −3, 9, −27, …

_54, 162, 486, 1,458_   32. 2, 6, 18, …

Problem Solving—Patterns   (Use after 4.7.)

Devise a plan that focuses on patterns and use it to solve each of the following problems.

1. Laura noticed that the house numbers on the left side of Vine Street were 5, 9, 13, …, while the numbers on the right side of the street were 2, 6, 10, …. She plans to visit her friend Cindy, who told her she lives in the twenty-second house on the left side of Vine Street. Since Laura does not want to count twenty-two houses, help her find Cindy's house number.

    $a_n = 5 + (n - 1)4$; $a_{22} = 89$; Cindy's house number is 89.

2. Chad also lives on Vine Street, and he told Laura that there are only four more houses (both right and left sides) after his before the street ends. If Vine Street has sixty-two houses with an equal number on each side, what could Chad's house number be?

    $62 \div 2 = 31$ houses on each side. He lives in the twenty-ninth house on either the left or right side; left side: $a_{29} = 117$; right side: $a_{29} = 114$; Chad's house number is 117 or 114.

3. What is the number of the last house (highest number) on Vine Street?

    left side: $a_{31} = 125$

4. One circuit of the bike path at the Cycle Park takes Richard 6 min. and Greg 7 min. to ride. If they leave the starting point at the same time, how long will it be before they are together again at the starting point?

    LCM of 6 and 7 = 42 min.

5. How many laps has each (Richard and Greg) made when they are together again at the starting point?

    Richard made 7 laps ($42 \div 6$); Greg made 6 laps ($42 \div 7$).

6. Are Richard and Greg ever together at other places on the circuit before they are together at the starting point again? Explain your answer.

   No; they are only one lap apart the first time they are together again at the starting point.

7. Anisha invested the $1,000 she received as a special gift on her eighth birthday. She noticed that her bank statements showed $1,000 at the start, $1,050 at the end of the first year, and $1,102.50 at the end of the second year, forming a geometric sequence. How much will she have in her account on her eighteenth birthday (which is the eleventh term in the sequence)?

   $r = 1.05$; $a_n = 1,000(1.05)^{n-1}$; $a_{11} = \$1,628.89$

8. How many cuts does it take to cut a 20 ft. board into ten pieces 2 ft. long each?

   It takes only 9 because the last cut generates 2 pieces.

9. If you cut a large piece of paper into six pieces with five cuts, then cut one of those into six pieces with five more cuts, and so on, how many pieces will you have after you have made thirty cuts?

   6 pieces with 5 cuts, 11 with 10, 16 with 15, 21 with 20, 26 with 25, and 31 pieces with 30 cuts

10. If Mr. Henry has $100 and grows his money yearly as in the following sequence, how long will it take for him to have at least $200: $100, $112, $125.44, …?

    $r = 1.12$; $a_n = 100(1.12)^{n-1}$; $a_8 = \$221.07$; he will have at least $200 after 7 yr.

Chapter 4 Review

Matching

a. base   c. exponent   f. prime number

b. composite   d. factor   g. power

      number   e. multiple

____a____ 1. the factor in repeated multiplication

____f____ 2. a number that has exactly two factors

____d____ 3. what 2 and 3 are to 6

____c____ 4. the number of times a factor is used in repeated multiplication

____g____ 5. a product in which each factor is the same

____e____ 6. what 12, 18, and 24 are to 6

____b____ 7. a number with more than two factors

Write T for true or F for false. If the statement is false, correct it.

____T____ 8. All numbers are divisible by one.

____F____ 9. One is a prime number.
             Prime numbers must be greater than one.

____F____ 10. All prime numbers are odd numbers.
             The even number 2 is prime.

____T____ 11. Any positive whole number raised to the zero power is equal to one.

____T____ 12. The smallest positive factor for any number is one.

____8, 16, 24, 32, 40____ 13. List the first five nonzero multiples of 8.

List in order all the factors of the given number.

14. 20
     1, 2, 4, 5, 10, 20

15. 72
     1, 2, 3, 4, 6, 8, 9, 12, 18, 24, 36, 72

Check each number for divisibility by 2, 3, 4, 5, 6, 8, 9, and 10. Put an X in the box if the divisibility test works.

		2	3	4	5	6	8	9	10
16.	75		X		X				
17.	144	X	X	X		X	X	X	
18.	90	X	X		X	X		X	X
19.	3,636	X	X	X		X		X	

Label each number as prime (P), composite (C), or neither (N).

___N___ 20. 0   ___P___ 21. 41   ___C___ 22. 63   ___N___ 23. 1

24. Write 3^4 as the product of repeated factors and simplify.
$3 \times 3 \times 3 \times 3 = 81$

Simplify.

___3^5 or 243___ 25. $3^2 \cdot 3^3$ ___12___ 26. $2^2 + 2^3$

___4^3 or 64___ 27. $4^2 \cdot 4$

Write the prime factorization of each number using exponential notation.

___$2^2 \cdot 7$___ 28. 28   ___$2^2 \cdot 5^2$___ 29. 100

___$2 \cdot 7 \cdot 13$___ 30. 182

Find the GCF and LCM of each set of numbers.

___GCF = 9; LCM = 180___ 31. 36, 45   ___GCF = 3; LCM = 360___ 32. 15, 18, 24

33. Danielle works at a store for an hourly wage of $8.20. She is paid time and a half for any hours over 40. Last week she worked 42 hr. Find the amount of her gross pay.
$352.60

Write the following numbers in base 10.

___18___ 34. 10010_2 ___117___ 35. 432_5

Write the following numbers in the indicated base.

___1110_2___ 36. 14 in base 2   ___135_7___ 37. 75 in base 7

Add or subtract in the indicated base.

___10001_2___ 38. $1011_2 + 110_2$ ___232_4___ 39. $321_4 - 23_4$ ___752_8___ 40. $516_8 + 234_8$

Cumulative Review 4

___d___   1. Write "8 less a number" as an algebraic expression.
   - a. $n - 8$
   - b. $n + 8$
   - c. $8n$
   - d. $8 - n$
   - e. none of these

___c___   2. Write "twice a number increased by 12" as an algebraic expression.
   - a. $2n - 12$
   - b. $12 - 2n$
   - c. $2n + 12$
   - d. $2(n + 12)$
   - e. none of these

___b___   3. Round 2,352 to the nearest hundred.
   - a. 2,350
   - b. 2,400
   - c. 2,300
   - d. 2,000
   - e. none of these

___a___   4. Estimate 58×97 by rounding.
   - a. 6,000
   - b. 5,000
   - c. 60,000
   - d. 5,626
   - e. none of these

___d___   5. Solve $x - 22 = 51$.
   - a. 29
   - b. −29
   - c. 1,122
   - d. 73
   - e. none of these

___b___   6. Write an equation for the following problem and then solve. Trina and Angela both have a collection of crystal bells. Trina has 8 more than Angela, and together they own 82. How many bells does Angela own?
   - a. $x + (x + 8) = 82; x = 45$
   - b. $x + (x + 8) = 82; x = 37$
   - c. $x + 8 = 82; x = 74$
   - d. $x + (x + 8) = 82; x = 33$
   - e. none of these

___e___   7. Solve $\frac{x}{8} = -4$.
   - a. $\frac{-1}{2}$
   - b. −4
   - c. 32
   - d. −2
   - e. none of these

___a___   8. Solve $3(a - 7) = -24$.
   - a. −1
   - b. −15
   - c. −3
   - d. 15
   - e. none of these

_____c_____ 9. Solve $4x + 8 + 3x = 15$.

    a. $\frac{23}{7}$ d. 7

    b. -1 e. none of these

    c. 1

_____c_____ 10. -18 is a member of which set of numbers? (State the most inclusive set.)

    a. natural   d. rationals

    b. whole   e. none of these

    c. integers

_____d_____ 11. $-\frac{6}{5}$ is a member of which set of numbers? (State the most inclusive set.)

    a. natural   d. rationals

    b. whole   e. none of these

    c. integers

_____a_____ 12. Which of the following numbers is a member of the solution set for $x + 6 < 8$?

    a. 1   d. 4

    b. 2   e. none of these

    c. 3

_____b_____ 13. Solve $x - 7 > 12$.

    a. $x < 5$ d. $x > 5$

    b. $x > 19$ e. none of these

    c. $x < -5$

_____d_____ 14. Solve $n + 18 - 4n \leq 6$.

    a. $n \leq 4$ d. $n \geq 4$

    b. $n \leq -4$ e. none of these

    c. $n \leq -8$

_____a_____ 15. Solve $14x \neq 728$.

    a. $x \neq 52$ d. $x \neq -714$

    b. $x \neq 714$ e. none of these

    c. $x \neq 10{,}192$

5 Rational Numbers

Creation Wonders—Trees   (Bible Activity; use after 5.1.)

From the universal destruction of the Flood, God brought forth a new and breathtaking face to the earth. High snow-capped mountains, vast oceans, rivers, lakes, and plant life of every description were once again singing of God's handiwork and bringing glory to His wonderful Person. Besides all the vegetation that provides abundant food, trees provide one of the most amazing building materials imaginable.

King David, in the midst of his joy over the return of the ark of the covenant to Jerusalem, wrote a beautiful psalm recorded in 1 Chronicles 16. In verses 31–33 he writes, "Let the heavens be glad, and let the earth rejoice: and let men say among the nations, The Lord reigneth. Let the sea roar, and the fulness thereof: let the fields rejoice, and all that is therein. Then shall the trees of the wood sing out at the presence of the Lord." Through the ages trees have been singing praises to the Creator. King Solomon covered much of the interior of the temple with cedar. These cedar trees, as well as fir trees, were purchased from King Hiram of Tyre and brought from Lebanon by a great workforce of thousands of people (1 Kings 5).

Although the earth abounds in a variety of trees, perhaps none are more fascinating than the giant redwoods of northern California. Most mature redwoods are greater than 300 ft. tall, and a few are over 360 ft. tall and 22 ft. in diameter at the base. These trees have a typical age of six hundred years, and some may have lived up to two thousand years. This would mean that trees standing in the forests of California today were saplings when men like Leonardo Fibonacci, Leonardo da Vinci, and Michelangelo were making history in mathematics and art. For centuries the mighty redwoods have being singing praise to their Creator.

1. What other important tree did Solomon use in the construction of the temple, besides cedar and fir (1 Kings 6:23)?
   olive

2. What wood did Moses prescribe for the construction of most of the wooden items in the wilderness tabernacle (Exod. 25:10)?
   shittim or acacia

3. What kind of tree did Christ condemn because it failed to bear fruit (Matt. 21:19)?
   fig

4. What kind of tree did Zaccheus climb in order to see Jesus passing by (Luke 19:4)?
   sycamore

5. What trees were used of God to give King David a signal to attack the Philistines (2 Sam. 5:23–24)?
   mulberry or balsam

6. Although Solomon did not measure the trees he purchased from Lebanon in board feet, that is how lumber is sold today. A board foot (BF) of wood is 144 in.³, or 1 in. × 12 in. × 12 in. A tree trunk that averages 2 ft. in diameter and is 64 ft. long contains about 200 ft.³ of wood. If just 30% of this is useful lumber, how many board feet does it provide? (Note: The bark and scrap pieces do have value as other products, such as manufactured panels called oriented strand board.)
   720 BF

And he shall be like a tree planted by the rivers of water, that bringeth forth his fruit in his season; his leaf also shall not wither; and whatsoever he doeth shall prosper.
Psalm 1:3

Rational Number Forms (Extra Practice; use after 5.1.)

Rename each fraction in lowest terms.

_____$\frac{3}{4}$_____ 1. $\frac{12}{16}$

_____$\frac{1}{2}$_____ 2. $\frac{21}{42}$

_____$\frac{2}{9}$_____ 3. $\frac{18}{81}$

_____$\frac{3}{10}$_____ 4. $\frac{15}{50}$

_____$\frac{8}{45}$_____ 5. $\frac{16}{90}$

_____$\frac{3}{5}$_____ 6. $\frac{39}{65}$

_____$\frac{7}{16}$_____ 7. $\frac{84}{192}$

_____$\frac{1}{5}$_____ 8. $\frac{125}{625}$

_____$\frac{3}{19}$_____ 9. $\frac{33}{209}$

Rename each mixed number as an improper fraction.

_____$\frac{17}{3}$_____ 10. $5\frac{2}{3}$

_____$-\frac{29}{8}$_____ 11. $-3\frac{5}{8}$

_____$\frac{87}{7}$_____ 12. $12\frac{3}{7}$

_____$-\frac{11}{4}$_____ 13. $-2\frac{3}{4}$

_____$\frac{155}{16}$_____ 14. $9\frac{11}{16}$

_____$-\frac{53}{6}$_____ 15. $-8\frac{5}{6}$

_____$\frac{113}{9}$_____ 16. $12\frac{5}{9}$

_____$\frac{77}{12}$_____ 17. $6\frac{5}{12}$

_____$\frac{59}{15}$_____ 18. $3\frac{14}{15}$

Rename each improper fraction as a mixed number.

_____$4\frac{12}{13}$_____ 19. $\frac{64}{13}$

_____$-3\frac{2}{5}$_____ 20. $-\frac{17}{5}$

_____$1\frac{1}{2}$_____ 21. $\frac{12}{8}$

_____$4\frac{1}{2}$_____ 22. $\frac{63}{14}$

_____$4\frac{4}{5}$_____ 23. $\frac{72}{15}$

_____$1\frac{1}{24}$_____ 24. $\frac{25}{24}$

_____$2\frac{31}{35}$_____ 25. $\frac{101}{35}$

_____$1\frac{5}{16}$_____ 26. $\frac{21}{16}$

_____$1\frac{1}{2}$_____ 27. $\frac{48}{32}$

Evaluate the following expressions when $w = -8$, $x = 2$, $y = -4$, and $z = 3$.

_____$64\frac{1}{2}$_____ 28. $64 - \frac{x}{y}$

_____$\frac{3}{8}$_____ 29. $-\frac{z}{w}$

_____$-\frac{1}{3}$_____ 30. $-\frac{xy}{wz}$

_____$\frac{1}{3}$_____ 31. $\frac{w}{xyz}$

_____$\frac{5}{16}$_____ 32. $\frac{1}{x^2} + \frac{1}{y^2}$

_____$-\frac{9}{2}$_____ 33. $\frac{6xz}{w}$

_____$-\frac{1}{5}$_____ 34. $\frac{4x}{5w}$

_____$-5\frac{1}{2}$_____ 35. $\frac{x^3}{y^2} - 2z$

_____$\frac{11}{24}$_____ 36. $\frac{1}{x} + \frac{1}{y} + \frac{1}{z} + \frac{1}{w}$

Calculator Skill 5 (Use after 5.3.)

written for the TI-30Xa

Mixed Numbers, Fractions, and Decimals with Applications

You have learned that a rational number has the form $\frac{a}{b}$, where a and b are integers and $b \neq 0$. But you will actually see rational numbers in any one of five different forms: proper fraction, improper fraction, mixed number, terminating decimal, or repeating decimal. The calculator lets us move efficiently between these various forms to use the one best suited for the context. The calculator has three function buttons that do all the navigating between these rational number forms.

$\boxed{A\frac{b}{c}}$ is used to enter a proper or improper fraction, as well as a mixed number, and to change improper fractions to mixed numbers.

$[d/c]$ is used to change mixed numbers to improper fractions.

$[F\leftrightarrow D]$ is used to move back and forth between fractions and decimals.

After entering an unreduced fraction with $\boxed{A\frac{b}{c}}$, you can reduce it by pushing $\boxed{=}$.

Example 1

Identify the keystrokes to enter for the given rational operations.

a. $\frac{3}{8} + \frac{5}{12}$

b. $4\frac{5}{16} - 2\frac{3}{5}$

Answer

a. Keystrokes: 3 $\boxed{A\frac{b}{c}}$ 8 $\boxed{+}$ 5 $\boxed{A\frac{b}{c}}$ 12 $\boxed{=}$. The result is $\frac{19}{24}$.

b. Keystrokes: 4 $\boxed{A\frac{b}{c}}$ 5 $\boxed{A\frac{b}{c}}$ 16 $\boxed{-}$ 2 $\boxed{A\frac{b}{c}}$ 3 $\boxed{A\frac{b}{c}}$ 5 $\boxed{=}$. The result is $1\frac{57}{80}$. You can change this to an improper fraction by using $[d/c]$. As an improper fraction the answer is $\frac{137}{80}$.

Example 2

Identify the keystrokes to enter for the given fraction, decimal, and percent problems.

a. $\frac{3}{8}$ is what percent of $2\frac{5}{8}$?

b. What is $\frac{5}{8}\%$ of $12\frac{1}{2}$?

Answer

a. Set up the algebra first: $p\left(2\frac{5}{8}\right) = \frac{3}{8}$, and solve for p. $p = \frac{3}{8} \div 2\frac{5}{8}$.

Keystrokes: 3 $\boxed{A\frac{b}{c}}$ 8 $\boxed{\div}$ 2 $\boxed{A\frac{b}{c}}$ 5 $\boxed{A\frac{b}{c}}$ 8 $\boxed{=}$. The result is $\frac{1}{7}$.

Find the decimal value by using $[F\leftrightarrow D]$. The decimal is approximately 0.143.
Change this to a percent by multiplying it by 100%: 0.143 $\boxed{\times}$ 100 $\boxed{=}$ 14.3%.

b. Keystrokes: 5 $\boxed{A\frac{b}{c}}$ 8 $[\%]$ $\boxed{\times}$ 12 $\boxed{A\frac{b}{c}}$ 1 $\boxed{A\frac{b}{c}}$ 2 $\boxed{=}$. The result is 0.078125.
Express this as a fraction by using $[F\leftrightarrow D]$. The result is $\frac{5}{64}$.

Perform the following calculations.

_____75%_____ 1. Express $\frac{45}{60}$ as a percent.

_____$\frac{9}{20}$_____ 2. Express 45% as a proper fraction.

_____$\frac{96}{125} = 0.768$_____ 3. Reduce $\frac{480}{625}$ to lowest terms and express it as a terminating decimal.

_____$0.\overline{714285}$_____ 4. Express $\frac{5}{7}$ as a repeating decimal.

_____$0.\overline{549}$_____ 5. Express $\frac{61}{111}$ as a repeating decimal.

_____$2\frac{31}{60} = \frac{151}{60}$_____ 6. Express $\frac{2}{3} + \frac{5}{4} + \frac{3}{5}$ as a mixed number and an improper fraction.

_____$1\frac{23}{36}$_____ 7. Express $\frac{5}{12} + \frac{22}{18}$ as a mixed number.

_____$\frac{675}{512}$_____ 8. Express $\frac{9}{16} \times 2\frac{11}{32}$ as an improper fraction.

_____$-2\frac{62}{105}$_____ 9. Express $5\frac{12}{35} - 7\frac{14}{15}$ as a mixed number.

_____$\frac{82}{7} = 11.\overline{714285}$_____ 10. Express $2\frac{9}{16} \div \frac{7}{32}$ as an improper fraction and a repeating decimal.

Use your calculator to solve.

11. Hunter owns $\frac{4}{9}$ of the stock of Bungee Inc., and his uncle owns $\frac{1}{3}$ of the stock. What percent of the stock does neither of them own?

    22.2%

12. A worker in a cabinet shop needs to cut five pieces of board with the following lengths: $2\frac{1}{8}$ in., $2\frac{5}{8}$ in., $5\frac{3}{16}$ in., $11\frac{5}{16}$ in., and $13\frac{7}{8}$ in. Every slice with his cut-off saw uses $\frac{1}{8}$ in. due to the kerf of the blade. Will he be able to get the five pieces from a 3 ft. board?

    Yes; there will be $\frac{3}{8}$ in. left over.

13. What percent of the bulk ingredients of a chocolate cake recipe is sugar? The following are the bulk ingredients: $1\frac{1}{2}$ c. butter, $1\frac{2}{3}$ c. sugar, $2\frac{2}{3}$ c. flour, $\frac{3}{4}$ c. ground almonds, $\frac{3}{8}$ c. unsweetened cocoa, and $\frac{1}{24}$ c. baking powder.

    23.8%

14. The management of a 6,000 acre grain farm likes to keep $\frac{2}{5}$ of the tillable land as fallow ground (no crops). If there are 85 acres of untillable land (ponds, marsh, etc.) and 20 acres of buildings, storage, and houses, how many acres would typically be fallow ground?

    2,358 acres

Problem Solving—Make a Sketch or Picture (Use after 5.3.)

Devise a plan for solving each of the following problems. Use a sketch to help you visualize how the information given in the problem relates to the unknown. Solve and check that your answer is reasonable.

1. Three ditch diggers working together and sharing the work equally can dig a certain ditch in five days. But after the first day of work, one of them develops a bad back, leaving the other two to finish the job. How many days will it take the two diggers to finish?

   6 days

2. A slow-moving bug is climbing a 15 ft. pole to reach a critical food source. It manages to climb 3 ft. each day, but at night it slides back down 1 ft. How many days will it take the bug to reach the top and get the food?

   7 days

3. There are 25 men who each have a locker. All locker doors are closed. The first man opens every door. Then the second man closes every other locker beginning with his own (locker 2). The third man changes the open/closed state of every third locker. The fourth man changes the state of every fourth locker. If this continues until all 25 have changed the doors, which lockers are open at the end? (Hint: A piece of graph paper makes a good tool to see what happens.)

   open: 1, 4, 9, 16, and 25 (all perfect squares)

4. When traveling on vacation, Mr. Lopez does not want to drive more than 400 mi. a day. One day there are three sites that the family wants to see. They must drive 22 mi., 18 mi., and 15 mi. off the interstate one way to reach these sites. What is the maximum number of miles they will travel on the interstate that day?

   290 mi.

5. A football team, the Tigers, started with the ball on their 35 yd. line. The following plays took place over the next eight downs. Where will the Tigers be on the field at the end of these eight downs? (A football field is 100 yd. long, measuring 0–50 yd. and then 50–0 yd. as you move from your end of the field to your opponent's end of the field.)

   run: 6 yd. gain, run: 2 yd. loss, run: 5 yd. gain, run: 2 yd. gain, pass: 19 yd. gain, run: 2 yd. gain, pass: 7 yd. gain, run: 4 yd. loss
   on the opponent's 30 yd. line

6. Three pieces of rope placed end-to-end on the ground have a combined length of 155 ft. If they are placed side by side, the longest piece stretches 24 ft. more than the medium-sized piece, while the shortest piece is 16 ft. shorter than the medium-sized piece. What are their lengths?

   longest: 73 ft., medium: 49 ft., and shortest: 33 ft.

7. Jared has a 3 gal. container and a 5 gal. container, but he needs to measure exactly 4 gal. of water. If he has an unlimited supply of water and can discard any amount he wants, how can he measure out 4 gal. with his containers?

   (Answers may vary.) He can pour the 3 gal. container into the 5 gal. container twice until it is full. This will leave 1 gal. in the 3 gal. container. He can empty the 5 gal. container and pour the 1 gal. into it. Then he can refill the 3 gal. container and pour it into the 5 gal. container to make 4 gal.

Patterns with Fractions (Enhanced Practice; use after 5.3.)

The decimal form of $\frac{1}{9}$ is $0.\overline{1}$. To determine the decimal equivalent for another fraction whose denominator is 9, multiply the numerator by $0.\overline{1}$.

Example 1
Convert $\frac{6}{9}$ to a decimal.

Answer
$\frac{6}{9} = 6 \cdot \frac{1}{9} = 6 \cdot 0.\overline{1} = 0.\overline{6}$

Convert the following fractions to decimals. Use the multiplication procedure when possible.

__0.25__ 1. $\frac{1}{4}$ __0.75__ 2. $\frac{3}{4}$

__0.2__ 3. $\frac{1}{5}$ __0.4__ 4. $\frac{2}{5}$

__0.8__ 5. $\frac{4}{5}$ __0.125__ 6. $\frac{1}{8}$

__0.375__ 7. $\frac{3}{8}$ __0.625__ 8. $\frac{5}{8}$

__0.875__ 9. $\frac{7}{8}$ __$0.\overline{09}$__ 10. $\frac{1}{11}$

__$0.\overline{18}$__ 11. $\frac{2}{11}$ __$0.\overline{27}$__ 12. $\frac{3}{11}$

__$0.\overline{36}$__ 13. $\frac{4}{11}$ __$0.\overline{45}$__ 14. $\frac{5}{11}$

_____0.$\overline{54}$_____ 15. $\frac{6}{11}$

_____0.$\overline{63}$_____ 16. $\frac{7}{11}$

_____0.$\overline{72}$_____ 17. $\frac{8}{11}$

_____0.$\overline{81}$_____ 18. $\frac{9}{11}$

_____0.$\overline{90}$_____ 19. $\frac{10}{11}$

_____0.$\overline{142857}$_____ 20. $\frac{1}{7}$

_____0.$\overline{285714}$_____ 21. $\frac{2}{7}$

_____0.$\overline{714285}$_____ 22. $\frac{5}{7}$

23. Compare your answers for exercises 20–22. What pattern do you find?
All digits are the same and stay in the same order relative to each other, but the starting number changes.

Once you have found the pattern, the decimal form of $\frac{n}{7}$ is easy to find. You will need to memorize the pattern of digits for $\frac{n}{7}$, 0.$\overline{142857}$. The first digit of the fraction $\frac{n}{7}$ can be found by multiplying the numerator of the given fraction times 14 and using the first digit of this product as the first digit of the decimal form.

Example 2
Convert $\frac{4}{7}$ to a decimal.

Answer
$4 \times 14 = 56$, so 5 is the first digit in the decimal. The 5 is followed by 7, which is followed by 1428 from the front of the repeating sequence: $\frac{4}{7} = 0.\overline{571428}$.

_____0.$\overline{428571}$_____ 24. Use this method to convert $\frac{3}{7}$ to a decimal.

Solving Problems Using Proportions (Enhanced Practice; use after 5.5.)

1. An architect is making a model of a building he designed. If the scale is 1 in. to 25 ft. and the building is to be 210 ft. high, how high should the model be?

   8.4 in.

2. When making ice cream, Mr. Johnson normally uses 2 bags of almonds for every 3 gal. of ice cream. How many gallons of ice cream can he make with 13 bags of almonds?

   $19\frac{1}{2}$ gal.

3. A recipe calls for three eggs, but Emily has only two. She will have to rewrite the recipe. Determine the amount of each ingredient she will need in the new recipe.

Original Recipe	Converted Recipe
3 eggs	2 eggs
2 cups flour	$1\frac{1}{3}$ cups flour
$\frac{3}{4}$ cup cocoa	$\frac{1}{2}$ cup cocoa
$\frac{1}{2}$ teaspoon salt, baking soda, and baking powder	$\frac{1}{3}$ teaspoon salt, baking soda, and baking powder
$\frac{1}{3}$ cup vegetable oil	$\frac{2}{9}$ cup vegetable oil
1 cup sugar	$\frac{2}{3}$ cup sugar

4. If Maria and Amy can color three dozen Easter eggs in 2 hr., how many can they color in 5 hr.?

   $7\frac{1}{2}$ dozen

5. Andrew plays basketball for his school team. If he averages 18 points per game, how many games would it take him to score 1,000 points?

   56 games

6. Jenn's mom served six children from a half gallon of ice cream. How much ice cream will she need to serve twenty-four children?

   2 gal.

Pascal's Triangle (Enrichment; use after 5.6.)

Although Blaise Pascal did not originate the triangular array of numbers that now bears his name, he placed it on a theoretical standing of great significance for the science of probability. He referred to it as the *arithmetic triangle* and wrote a paper in 1653 addressing many of the properties of this now-famous array of numbers. Each entry (other than the ones) is found by adding the two entries to the right and left of it in the row directly above.

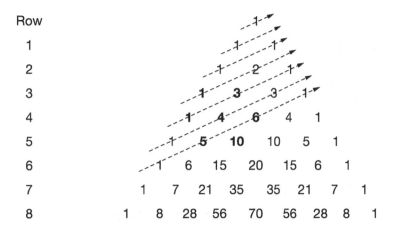

Row
1
2
3
4
5
6
7
8

1. Find the sum of the numbers in each of the first seven horizontal rows of the triangle.
    row 1: 2, row 2: 4, row 3: 8, row 4: 16, row 5: 32, row 6: 64, row 7: 128

2. Write the sums found in exercise 1 as powers of two.
    $2 = 2^1$, $4 = 2^2$, $8 = 2^3$, $16 = 2^4$, $32 = 2^5$, $64 = 2^6$, $128 = 2^7$

3. Use your work from exercises 1 and 2 to write a formula for the sum of the entries in the *n*th row.
    sum of the entries in the *n*th row = 2^n

4. Find the sums along the diagonals shown. Draw two more upward diagonals and find the sums along these. What is this sequence of numbers called?
    sums: 1, 1, 2, 3, 5, 8, 13; additional sums: 21, 34; Fibonacci numbers

5. In row 4 the second entry is a 4. Add 4 and all of the numbers that surround it in the one row above and below it as well as in the same row. How does the sum compare to the number in row 6 directly below the 4 in row 4?
    $4 + 1 + 1 + 3 + 6 + 10 + 5 = 30$, which is two times the 15 in row 6.

6. Choose a different position on Pascal's triangle and repeat the procedure used in exercise 5. Verify that the sum is twice the number directly under the number you started with.
    Answers will vary.

Chapter 5 Review

Fill in the blank.

_____products_____ 1. Two equivalent fractions will have equal ___ when you cross-multiply.

_____improper_____ 2. A(n) ___ fraction has a value of one or more.

_____proper_____ 3. A(n) ___ fraction has a value less than one.

_____1_____ 4. A fraction in lowest terms is one in which the GCF of the numerator and denominator is ___.

_____repeating; terminating_____ 5. Every rational number can be written either as a ___ decimal or as a ___ decimal.

_____rational; irrational_____ 6. The set of real numbers is made up of the set of ___ numbers and the set of ___ numbers.

_____extremes_____ 7. In the proportion $\frac{a}{b} = \frac{c}{d}$, a and d are called the ___.

Matching

__c__ 8. ratio

__d__ 9. rate

__a__ 10. proportion

a. a comparison of two equivalent ratios
b. a comparison of a number to 100
c. a comparison of two numbers
d. a comparison of two different units
e. a comparison of lengths

Write T for true or F for false.

__F__ 11. Every whole number is a natural number.

__F__ 12. $2.57 + 8.62 = 8.62 + 2.57$ is an example of the Distributive Property of real numbers.

__T__ 13. When $\frac{5}{9}$ is converted to decimal form, the result is a repeating decimal.

__F__ 14. The integers are closed with respect to the operation of division.

Rename each fraction in lowest terms.

_____$\frac{5}{7}$_____ 15. $\frac{15}{21}$

_____$\frac{9}{10}$_____ 16. $\frac{54}{60}$

Rename each improper fraction as a mixed or whole number.

_____9_____ 17. $\frac{117}{13}$

_____$18\frac{1}{4}$_____ 18. $\frac{73}{4}$

Rename each mixed number as an improper fraction.

_____$\frac{24}{7}$_____ 19. $3\frac{3}{7}$

_____$\frac{93}{13}$_____ 20. $7\frac{2}{13}$

Compare the given fractions, using >, <, or =.

__>__ 21. $\frac{9}{16} \square \frac{11}{25}$

__=__ 22. $\frac{14}{24} \square \frac{35}{60}$

__>__ 23. $\frac{3}{4} \square \frac{39}{56}$

__=__ 24. $\frac{7}{91} \square \frac{1}{13}$

Convert the following fractions to decimals.

__0.625__ 25. $\frac{5}{8}$

__$0.\overline{857142}$__ 26. $\frac{6}{7}$

Convert the following decimals to fractions in lowest terms.

__$\frac{3}{4}$__ 27. 0.75

__$\frac{9}{11}$__ 28. $0.\overline{81}$

Solve the following proportions.

__$a = 120$__ 29. $\frac{5}{6} = \frac{a}{144}$

__$b = 99$__ 30. $\frac{5}{9} = \frac{55}{b}$

__$x = 6.25$__ 31. $\frac{10}{16} = \frac{x}{10}$

__$y = 24$__ 32. $\frac{15}{y} = \frac{25}{40}$

Find the unit rate.

__63 km/hr.__ 33. $\frac{441 \text{ km}}{7 \text{ hr.}}$

__$0.13/in.__ 34. $\frac{\$1.69}{13 \text{ in.}}$

__$5.98/yd.__ 35. 6 yd. of material for $35.88

__35 mi./gal.__ 36. 140 mi. on 4 gal.

Solve.

37. Kathy can read six books in ten days. How many books can she read in fifteen days?

9 books

38. If the student-to-teacher ratio at Landmark Christian School is 12 to 1 and there are 23 teachers at the school, how many students attend the school?

276 students

Cumulative Review 5

<u> c </u>   1. Simplify $-8 + 23$.
       a. -15 d. -31
       b. 31 e. none of these
       c. 15

<u> a </u>   2. Simplify $-516 \div (-4)$.
       a. 129 d. -520
       b. $2,064$ e. none of these
       c. $-2,064$

<u> d </u>   3. Simplify $5 + (-6 - 9)8 - 27$.
       a. -100 d. -142
       b. -46 e. none of these
       c. 152

<u> e </u>   4. Solve $5x = -300$.
       a. 60 d. -6
       b. -305 e. none of these
       c. 6

<u> b </u>   5. Solve $3x - 47 = -71$.
       a. $\frac{-118}{3}$ d. -27
       b. -8 e. none of these
       c. 70

<u> a </u>   6. Solve $-7x + 2 > -61$.
       a. $x < 9$ d. $x < -\frac{59}{7}$
       b. $x > \frac{59}{7}$ e. none of these
       c. $x > -9$

<u> b </u>   7. Which of the following numbers is prime?
       a. 36 d. 133
       b. 59 e. none of these
       c. 117

<u> c </u>   8. Give the prime factorization of 728.
       a. $2 \cdot 3^2 \cdot 13$ d. $2^3 \cdot 7 \cdot 19$
       b. $2^2 \cdot 3^2 \cdot 7^2$ e. none of these
       c. $2^3 \cdot 7 \cdot 13$

_____e_____ 9. Give the prime factorization of 345.
  a. $3 \cdot 5 \cdot 19$
  b. $3 \cdot 5 \cdot 17$
  c. $3 \cdot 115$

  d. $3 \cdot 5 \cdot 13$
  e. none of these

_____d_____ 10. Find the GCF of 154 and 294.
  a. 11
  b. 7
  c. 2

  d. 14
  e. none of these

_____a_____ 11. What are the next three numbers in the sequence 8, 12, 16, 20, …?
  a. 24, 28, 32
  b. 24, 30, 36
  c. 24, 31, 38

  d. 25, 31, 37
  e. none of these

_____c_____ 12. What are the next three numbers in the sequence –2, 4, –8, 16, …?
  a. –32, –64, –128
  b. 32, –64, 128
  c. –32, 64, –128

  d. 32, 64, 128
  e. none of these

_____b_____ 13. What type of sequence is $\frac{1}{3}, \frac{1}{9}, \frac{1}{27}, \frac{1}{81}, \ldots$?
  a. harmonic
  b. geometric
  c. arithmetic

  d. Fibonacci
  e. none of these

_____c_____ 14. Identify the property used: $a \cdot (b \cdot c) = (a \cdot b) \cdot c$.
  a. Associative Property of Addition
  b. Commutative Property of Multiplication
  c. Associative Property of Multiplication
  d. Inverse Property of Addition
  e. none of these

_____e_____ 15. Use the Distributive Property to simplify $5(x - 8)$.
  a. $5x - 8$
  b. $5x + 40$
  c. $5x + 8$

  d. $5x - 13$
  e. none of these

6 Operations on Rational Numbers

Creation Wonders—Whales   (Bible Activity; use after 6.1.)

Among the living creatures created by God to bring Him glory, we find some that are huge. The elephant exceeds all other land animals in size and weight, but it cannot compare in size to a whale. Elephants weigh several tons, but blue whales can be over 100 ft. long and weigh around 150 tn. Though whales live in the ocean, they are mammals, not fish. They have lungs and hair rather than gills and scales, and their offspring are born, not hatched.

The blowhole on top of a whale is actually its "nose," and blowing out water clears the nose so the whale can breathe before returning to the depths of the sea. Whales live in families, called pods, and remain in the same pod for their entire life. Like many mammals, whales communicate with each other by using high-pitched whistles, squeaks, clicks, and groans. Certain whales compensate for their poor visibility in the water by a type of radar called echolocation, and some make a very low-pitched sound that can be heard at great distances. Whales belong to the same order (Cetacea) as dolphins, and they share many similar characteristics with dolphins. There are over eighty kinds of whales and dolphins.

The Bible says that the prophet Jonah was swallowed by a great fish prepared by God, not a whale. (Though the word "whale's" is used in Matthew 12:40, it refers to a great sea creature rather than a whale specifically.) God needed to fashion some special characteristics for that fish, especially so Jonah would not get digested during his three-day stay.

Human fascination with whales through the centuries makes sense because of the acrobatic antics, stream-lined beauty, and immense size of these largest of God's creatures.

1. How many hours was Jonah in the belly of the great fish?
   72 hr.

2. Read about leviathan in Job 41. Do you think this strange creature is a whale? Why or why not?
   It is not a whale since whales do not have scales. (Answers will vary.)

3. Genesis 1 is very specific about the fact that on the fifth day God created life to inhabit the seas and fly through the air. Besides birds, what animals are mentioned?
   whales or great sea creatures

4. In Ezekiel 32 the prophet records God's warning of judgment on Pharaoh, king of Egypt. What land animal does Pharaoh think he is like? What sea animal is he compared to? What does Ezekiel say will happen to this animal that is symbolic of what will happen to Egypt?
   a lion; a whale or a sea monster or dragon; It will be caught in a net and its carcass thrown to the animals.

5. An object in water is buoyed up by a force equal to the weight of the water it displaces. So an object floating just below the surface of the water would displace the same weight of water as the object itself weighs. Boats float above the water because they weigh less than the water they displace. If a whale weighs 150 tn. and is floating just below the surface of the ocean, how many gallons of water does it displace? (Water weighs 8.34 lb./gal.)
   35,971 gal.

For as Jonas was three days and three nights in the whale's belly; so shall the Son of man be three days and three nights in the heart of the earth. Matthew 12:40

Addition and Subtraction of Rational Numbers (Extra Practice; use after 6.1.)

Add or subtract. If necessary, rename in lowest terms.

__$\frac{4}{5}$__ 1. $\frac{3}{5} + \frac{1}{5}$

__$\frac{1}{2}$__ 2. $\frac{5}{12} + \frac{1}{12}$

__$-\frac{3}{40}$__ 3. $\frac{5}{8} - \frac{7}{10}$

__$5\frac{5}{12}$__ 4. $3\frac{2}{3} + 1\frac{3}{4}$

__$1\frac{15}{16}$__ 5. $5\frac{9}{16} - 3\frac{5}{8}$

__$1\frac{17}{48}$__ 6. $\frac{15}{16} + \frac{5}{12}$

__$\frac{1}{2}$__ 7. $\frac{9}{5} - 1\frac{3}{10}$

__$-1\frac{13}{45}$__ 8. $-\frac{11}{15} - \frac{5}{9}$

__$\frac{221}{264}$__ 9. $\frac{7}{24} + \frac{18}{33}$

__$1\frac{1}{12}$__ 10. $\frac{1}{4} + \frac{1}{3} + \frac{1}{2}$

__$-\frac{1}{42}$__ 11. $\frac{9}{14} - \frac{3}{7} - \frac{5}{21}$

__0__ 12. $\frac{5}{24} - \left(\frac{3}{8} - \frac{1}{6}\right)$

__$2\frac{1}{24}$__ 13. $4\frac{1}{6} + 7\frac{1}{8} - 9\frac{1}{4}$

__$7\frac{1}{2}$__ 14. $\frac{56}{12} + \frac{45}{54} + 2$

__$\frac{7}{20}$__ 15. $\frac{2}{7} + \frac{9}{42} - \frac{4}{35} - \frac{1}{28}$

__$1\frac{6}{13}$__ 16. $\frac{62}{78} + \frac{104}{156}$

Perform the indicated operations.

__4.918__ 17. $1.245 + 3.673$

__11.6__ 18. $21.45 - 9.85$

__0.2909__ 19. $0.0239 + 0.267$

__1.61__ 20. $2.25 + 3.69 - 4.33$

__0.302__ 21. $0.003 + 0.034 + 0.265$

__-3.093__ 22. $1.486 - 4.579$

__-4.002__ 23. $-12.785 - (6.342 - 15.125)$

__$0.\overline{63}$__ 24. $0.\overline{18} + 0.\overline{45}$

__$0.\overline{73}$__ 25. $0.\overline{50} + 0.\overline{23}$

Pascal's Triangle and Fractions (Enrichment; use after 6.1.)

Pascal's triangle has many interesting properties, some of which you discovered in the Pascal's triangle activity in Chapter 5. You can also find properties related to fractions using Pascal's triangle. If the rows of Pascal's triangle are left justified, then it appears as follows.

Row									
	1								
1	1	1							
2	1	2	1						
3	1	3	3	1					
4	1	4	6	4	1				
5	1	5	10	10	5	1			
6	1	6	15	20	15	6	1		
7	1	7	21	35	35	21	7	1	
8	1	8	28	56	70	56	28	8	1

A rectangle can be created around a section of numbers. Let the second column be the left side of the rectangle, and let the upper right corner of the rectangle be the 1 in the row. Consider the rectangle outlined above.

Using this rectangle, let $a = 5$, $b = 10$, $c = 10$, $d = 5$, $e = 1$, $f = 6$, $g = 15$, ..., $t = 56$.
Let w = the number of columns ($w = 5$), and let u = the number of rows ($u = 4$).

a	b	c	d	e
f	g	h	i	j
k	l	m	n	o
p	q	r	s	t

Evaluate the following algebraic expressions using the numbers from Pascal's triangle that correspond to the variables in the rectangle above. Express answers in lowest terms.

$\dfrac{5}{4}$ _____ 1. $\dfrac{w}{u}$

$\dfrac{5}{4}$ _____ 2. $\dfrac{s}{t}$

$\dfrac{5}{4}$ _____ 3. $\dfrac{a}{p} + \dfrac{b}{q} + \dfrac{c}{r} + \dfrac{d}{s} + \dfrac{e}{t}$

4. What do you notice about the answers to exercises 1–3?
   They are all the same.

5. Form a rectangle using rows 4–6 of Pascal's triangle in the same manner that the rectangle using rows 5–8 was formed (again using the second column as the left side of the rectangle). Find the value of the same three ratios that were given in exercises 1–3. Does the same pattern occur? Show all of your work.
   Yes, the same pattern occurs.

6. Make a conjecture about your observations in this activity.
   The ratios of $\dfrac{\text{number of columns}}{\text{number of rows}}$, $\dfrac{\text{second-to-last element in the bottom row}}{\text{last element in the bottom row}}$, and the sum of the ratios of the corresponding elements in the top and bottom rows are always equal to each other.

Multiplication of Fractions (Enhanced Practice; use after 6.2.)

Students will need rulers and colored pencils.

Multiplication can be signified by the word *of*. $\frac{1}{3}$ of $\frac{1}{2}$ means $\frac{1}{3} \times \frac{1}{2}$. Follow the steps below, using a rectangle to picture the multiplication process.

1. Picture the second fraction by drawing horizontal dividing lines and shading the appropriate part with a colored pencil.

2. Picture the first fraction by drawing vertical dividing lines and shading the appropriate part with a second colored pencil.

3. Find what fraction of the whole is shaded by both colors. $\frac{1}{6}$ of the rectangle contains both shades of pencil. Therefore, $\frac{1}{3} \times \frac{1}{2} = \frac{1}{6}$.

Example

Find the product of $\frac{1}{3} \times \frac{1}{4}$ by using rectangular shading.

Answer

$\frac{1}{12}$ of the rectangle is shaded by both colors. Therefore, $\frac{1}{3} \times \frac{1}{4} = \frac{1}{12}$.

Multiply by using rectangular shading.

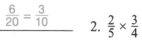

$\underset{\displaystyle \frac{5}{32}}{\underline{\hspace{3cm}}}$ 1. $\frac{5}{8} \times \frac{1}{4}$

$\underset{\displaystyle \frac{6}{20} = \frac{3}{10}}{\underline{\hspace{3cm}}}$ 2. $\frac{2}{5} \times \frac{3}{4}$
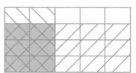

$\underset{\displaystyle \frac{6}{15} = \frac{2}{5}}{\underline{\hspace{3cm}}}$ 3. $\frac{2}{3} \times \frac{3}{5}$

$\underset{\displaystyle \frac{2}{24} = \frac{1}{12}}{\underline{\hspace{3cm}}}$ 4. $\frac{2}{3} \times \frac{1}{8}$
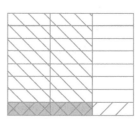

$\underset{\displaystyle \frac{6}{12} = \frac{1}{2}}{\underline{\hspace{3cm}}}$ 5. $\frac{3}{4} \times \frac{2}{3}$
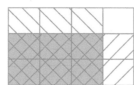

Multiplication and Division of Rational Numbers

(Extra Practice; use after 6.3.)

Multiply or divide. If necessary, rename in lowest terms.

$\dfrac{1}{15}$ 1. $\dfrac{3}{5} \times \dfrac{1}{9}$

5   2. $\dfrac{5}{12} \div \dfrac{1}{12}$

$\dfrac{7}{16}$ 3. $\dfrac{5}{8} \times \dfrac{7}{10}$

$-\dfrac{25}{6}$ 4. $-3\dfrac{1}{3} \times 1\dfrac{1}{4}$

$-\dfrac{3}{2}$ 5. $\dfrac{9}{16} \div \dfrac{-3}{8}$

$\dfrac{9}{4}$ 6. $\dfrac{15}{16} \div \dfrac{5}{12}$

$\dfrac{13}{18}$ 7. $\dfrac{5}{9} \times 1\dfrac{3}{10}$

$-\dfrac{21}{25}$ 8. $-\dfrac{7}{15} \div \dfrac{5}{9}$

$\dfrac{87}{5}$ 9. $4\dfrac{1}{7} \times 4\dfrac{1}{5}$

$\dfrac{3}{2}$ 10. $1\dfrac{3}{4} \times \dfrac{6}{7}$

$-\dfrac{8}{25}$ 11. $-\dfrac{2}{5} \div 1\dfrac{1}{4}$

7   12. $3\dfrac{1}{9} \times 2\dfrac{1}{4}$

$\dfrac{3}{20}$ 13. $\dfrac{7}{24} \times \dfrac{18}{35}$

$\dfrac{1}{6}$ 14. $\dfrac{1}{4} \times \dfrac{1}{3} \div \dfrac{1}{2}$

$\dfrac{5}{12}$ 15. $\dfrac{7}{10} \times \dfrac{13}{21} \times \dfrac{25}{26}$

5   16. $\dfrac{5}{24} \div \left(\dfrac{3}{8} \times \dfrac{1}{9} \right)$

$\dfrac{5}{4}$ 17. $1\dfrac{1}{8} \div \dfrac{3}{5} \times \dfrac{2}{3}$

$\dfrac{71}{18}$ 18. $\dfrac{56}{12} \times \dfrac{45}{54} + \dfrac{1}{18}$

$\dfrac{2}{3}$ 19. $\left(\dfrac{2}{7} \div \dfrac{9}{42} \right) - \left(\dfrac{1}{42} \div \dfrac{1}{28} \right)$

$-\dfrac{31}{26}$ 20. $\dfrac{62}{78} \div \dfrac{-104}{156}$

$\dfrac{17}{3}$ 21. $2\dfrac{1}{8} \times 2\dfrac{2}{3}$

$\dfrac{169}{30}$ 22. $2\dfrac{3}{5} \times 2\dfrac{1}{6}$

$-\dfrac{73}{3}$ 23. $-4\dfrac{9}{16} \times 5\dfrac{1}{3}$

$\dfrac{1}{8}$ 24. $\dfrac{7}{10} \div 6\dfrac{2}{5} \times 1\dfrac{1}{7}$

Perform the indicated operations.

_____3.844_____ 25. 1.24×3.1

_____197.8_____ 26. 21.5×9.2

_____0.125_____ 27. $0.025 \div 0.2$

_____−0.4556_____ 28. $22.78 \times (-0.02)$

_____−313.5_____ 29. -125.4×2.5

_____110.24_____ 30. $4.63 \div 0.042$

_____0.9189_____ 31. 0.0045×204.2

_____37_____ 32. $4.625 \div 0.125$

_____−22.08_____ 33. $-3.2(8.28 \div 1.2)$

_____0.37_____ 34. $1.48 \div 4$

_____−1,228_____ 35. $-24.56 \div 0.02$

_____130.2_____ 36. $4.2(12.4 \times 2.5)$

_____48.72_____ 37. $0.35(241.4 - 102.2)$

_____21.35_____ 38. $(24.4 \times 0.42) \div 0.48$

_____0.15_____ 39. $0.25 \times 0.75 \times 0.8$

_____31.416_____ 40. $2.2 \times 3.4 \times 4.2$

Problem Solving—Divide and Conquer (Use after 6.7.)

Solve each of the following problems by solving several smaller problems that are essential to the solution of the whole problem.

1. How many sheets can a copier reproduce in 5 min. if it makes a copy every $1\frac{1}{9}$ sec.?

   270 sheets

2. If a sheet of $8\frac{1}{2}$ in. × 11 in. paper is $\frac{1}{256}$ in. thick, how many sheets will fit comfortably in a box that is 2 in. deep?

   512 sheets

3. How many kilowatt-hours (kWh) of electrical energy did a household use if each kWh costs $8\frac{3}{8}$¢ and the total bill before tax was $124.80?

   1,490.1 kWh

4. Five-eighths of an elementary class is boys. If three boys were transferred to other classes and three girls were transferred into the class, the class would be one-half boys and one-half girls. How many students are in this class?

   24 students

5. The starting price and the daily changes for a common share of PetroGlobe stock are given in the table. What was the closing price?

Daily Change						
Opening	Monday	Tuesday	Wednesday	Thursday	Friday	Closing
35.13	+0.38	−1.25	−0.25	+0.88	+3.63	38.52

6. If sound travels at approximately $\frac{1}{5}$ mi./sec., how many yards away is a lightning strike if you hear the thunder $1\frac{1}{8}$ sec. after the flash?

396 yd.

7. The earth's diameter is approximately 7.9×10^3 mi. If the sun's diameter is 109 times larger than the earth's diameter, what is the diameter of the sun?

8.611×10^5 mi.

8. The earth's mass is about 6.6×10^{21} tn. If the sun's mass is 3.33×10^5 times greater than the earth's mass, what is the mass of the sun?

2.1978×10^{27} tn.

9. Mr. Patterson's stock portfolio consists of $\frac{1}{3}$ small-cap stocks and $\frac{2}{3}$ large-cap stocks. If he were to sell 125 shares of his large-cap stocks and replace them with 125 shares of small-cap stocks, then his portfolio would have an equal amount of both types. How many shares are in Mr. Patterson's stock portfolio?

750 shares

Calculator Skill 6 (Use after 6.8.)

written for the TI-30Xa

Applications of Scientific Notation

Scientific notation enables us to compute with very large or very small numbers and still use a calculator with a limited number of characters. Instead of entering the number 2,450,000,000 in its standard form, you could enter it using scientific notation. Remember that $2,450,000,000 = 2.45 \times 10^9$. While this can be entered as 2 $\boxed{.}$ 45 $\boxed{\times}$ 10 $\boxed{y^x}$ 9, the $\boxed{EE}$ key can be used instead of the sequence $\boxed{\times}$ 10 $\boxed{y^x}$. The shortened keystrokes 2 $\boxed{.}$ 45 $\boxed{EE}$ 9 reflect the way numbers in scientific notation are displayed on your calculator. Entering the keystrokes 2 $\boxed{.}$ 45 $\boxed{\times}$ 10 $\boxed{EE}$ 9, interpreted by the calculator as $2.45(10 \times 10^9)$, produces the erroneous entry of 2.45×10^{10}. The TI-30Xa calculator is limited by a maximum exponent of 99. Any calculation that gives a number with an exponent that is greater than 99 will result in an error message.

Scientists have developed a number of physical constants, some of which are very large numbers and some of which are very small numbers that need to be expressed in scientific notation. Three of these are given below.

Planck's constant: The fundamental constant of quantum physics is 6.626×10^{-34} joule-seconds. The energy of light is the product of the wavelength (expressed as frequency) and Planck's constant. This constant is a very small number.

Avogadro's number: The number of molecules (or atoms) of a substance in one mole is 6.0225×10^{23} molecules. (A mole is the amount of a compound whose mass in grams equals its molecular weight.) This constant is a very large number.

Speed of light: The speed of light in a vacuum is 3.0×10^5 km/sec. or 1.864×10^5 mi./sec.

1. List the calculator keystrokes you would use to find how many miles light travels in one hour, in one day, and in one year. Give the results in scientific notation. Then give the word form of the standard numeral of one light-year. (Hint: It may help to have your calculator in SCI mode [$\boxed{2nd}$ 5].)
   hour: 1 $\boxed{.}$ 864 $\boxed{EE}$ 5 $\boxed{\times}$ 60 $\boxed{\times}$ 60 $\boxed{=}$; result: 6.7104×10^8 mi./hr.;
   day: 6 $\boxed{.}$ 7104 $\boxed{EE}$ 8 $\boxed{\times}$ 24 $\boxed{=}$; result: 1.610496×10^{10} mi./day;
   year: 1 $\boxed{.}$ 610496 $\boxed{EE}$ 10 $\boxed{\times}$ 365 $\boxed{=}$; result: 5.8783104×10^{12} mi./yr.;
   one light-year: five trillion, eight hundred seventy-eight billion, three hundred ten million, four hundred thousand miles

2. If the nearest star to the earth, Alpha Centauri, is 4.22 light-years away, how far is it in kilometers to this star?
   3.9924576×10^{13} km

3. If a spaceship can move at 144,000 km/hr. in empty space, how long would it take to get to Alpha Centauri?
   2.77254×10^8 hr. = 3.165×10^4 yr.

4. If the average distance from the earth to the sun is 93,000,000 mi., how many minutes does it take light from the sun to reach the earth?

8.315 min.

5. If an airline pilot logs 4,200 mi./day for each day of a five-day work week and if he works for 48 weeks a year, how many light-years will he travel during his thirty-five-year career?

6.002×10^{-6} light-years

6. If two towers are 15 km apart, how many seconds does it take light to travel between the towers?

5×10^{-5} sec.

7. It is approximately 795 million mi. from the earth to Saturn. Space probes send data and pictures back to the earth via radio waves that travel at 3.1×10^5 mi./sec. How many minutes does it take the information to get from Saturn back to the earth?

42.7 min.

8. If the frequency (cycles per second) of green light is about 6×10^{14}, what is the energy (in joules) of a photon of green light, based on the definition of Planck's constant?

3.9756×10^{-19} joules

Chapter 6 Review

Write T for true or F for false. If the statement is false, correct it.

___T___ 1. Multiplication and division are inverse operations.

___T___ 2. Before multiplying mixed numbers, you must change each mixed number to an improper fraction.

___F___ 3. When dividing fractions, you must use the reciprocal of the dividend.
  change "dividend" to "divisor"

___F___ 4. When adding or subtracting decimals, you should line up the numbers by the far right digit in each number.
  change "far right digit" to "decimal point"

___T___ 5. When adding or subtracting fractions, you must find a common denominator and form equivalent fractions before adding the numerators.

___F___ 6. Decimals that show a pattern, such as 0.242242224…, but do not terminate are called repeating decimals.
  change "repeating decimals" to "irrational numbers"

Perform the indicated operations and simplify.

___$1\frac{9}{28}$___ 7. $\frac{3}{4} + \frac{4}{7}$

___$\frac{1}{21}$___ 8. $\frac{5}{7} - \frac{2}{3}$

___$\frac{11}{24}$___ 9. $\frac{3}{8} - \frac{1}{4} + \frac{1}{3}$

___$1\frac{8}{11}$___ 10. $4\frac{4}{11} - 2\frac{7}{11}$

___$7\frac{5}{56}$___ 11. $2\frac{5}{7} + 4\frac{3}{8}$

___227.408___ 12. $45.018 + 182.39$

___70.21___ 13. $82 - 11.79$

___190.404___ 14. 49.2×3.87

_29,198.76_ 15. 918.2×31.8

_13.272_ 16. $65.3 \div 4.92$
(nearest thousandth)

_3.0925_ 17. $12.37 \div 4$

$\frac{5}{21}$ 18. $\frac{3}{7} \cdot \frac{5}{9}$

$\frac{10}{21}$ 19. $\frac{12}{21} \cdot \frac{15}{18}$

$\frac{1}{6}$ 20. $\frac{1}{8} \div \frac{3}{4}$

$\frac{35}{38}$ 21. $\frac{7}{8} \div \frac{19}{20}$

_26_ 22. $3\frac{1}{4} \times 8$

$5\frac{5}{8}$ 23. $1\frac{2}{3} \cdot 3\frac{3}{8}$

Evaluate.

_42.41_ 24. $7.21 + b$ when $b = 35.2$

_−1.917_ 25. $2k - 2.617$ when $k = 0.35$

$5\frac{2}{3}$ or $5.\overline{6}$ 26. $\frac{x}{3}$ when $x = 17$

$9\frac{2}{5}$ or 9.4 27. $\frac{47}{w}$ when $w = 5$

Simplify.

$\frac{5}{7}x + \frac{23}{42}$ 28. $\frac{5}{7}\left(x + \frac{2}{3}\right) + \frac{1}{14}$

$\frac{7}{10}y^2 + \frac{10}{7}y + \frac{14}{3}$ 29. $\frac{6}{5}y^2 + \frac{3}{7}y + 4 - \frac{1}{2}y^2 + y + \frac{2}{3}$

$-23.35a + 14.7b$ 30. $-4.15(a - 2b) + 6.4(-3a + b)$

$7.6x^2 + 3.37x + 4.23y$ 31. $7.6(x^2 + y) + 3.37(x - y)$

Solve.

_____$x = 3.8$_____ 32. $x + 3.9 = 7.7$

_____$y = 8.51$_____ 33. $y - 3.6 = 4.91$

_____$t = 9.2$_____ 34. $4.1t = 37.72$

_____$w = 34.86$_____ 35. $\frac{w}{4.2} = 8.3$

_____$x = \frac{1}{2}$_____ 36. $x + \frac{1}{3} = \frac{5}{6}$

_____$x = 1\frac{17}{24}$_____ 37. $x - \frac{5}{8} = \frac{13}{12}$

_____$a = \frac{2}{15}$_____ 38. $7a = \frac{14}{15}$

_____$c = 2\frac{1}{2}$_____ 39. $\frac{3}{4}c = 1\frac{7}{8}$

Perform the indicated operations. Leave answers in scientific notation.

_____8.67×10^9_____ 40. $(8.4 \times 10^9) + (2.7 \times 10^8)$

_____1.008×10^{-15}_____ 41. $(2.8 \times 10^{-9}) \times (3.6 \times 10^{-7})$

Write an equation and solve.

42. Three-fourths of the boys in the junior high school participate in the sports program. There are 27 boys who participate. How many boys are in the junior high?
$\frac{3}{4}x = 27;$ 36 boys

43. John has been working for his mother. She told him that if he works on Mondays, she will give him a dollar, and every day after that she will double his pay. What is his total pay for the week if he works five consecutive days?
$x = 1 + 2 + 4 + 8 + 16;$ $31

44. A pattern calls for $1\frac{3}{8}$ yd. of lace. If Jeannie has $\frac{3}{4}$ yd., how much more does she need?
$\frac{3}{4} + x = 1\frac{3}{8};$ $\frac{5}{8}$ yd.

Cumulative Review 6

_____d_____ 1. Subtract −87 − 38.
  a. −49
  b. 49
  c. 125

  d. −125
  e. none of these

_____a_____ 2. Multiply −7(14)(−12).
  a. 1,176
  b. −6
  c. −1,176

  d. 6
  e. none of these

_____c_____ 3. Identify the property used: $a(b + c) = a(c + b)$.
  a. Distributive
  b. Associative
  c. Commutative

  d. Inverse
  e. none of these

_____e_____ 4. Which of the following equations illustrates the Inverse Property of Multiplication?
  a. $3(2 + 6) = 6 + 18$
  b. $7 + (−7) = 0$
  c. $(4 + 6) + 2 = 4 + (6 + 2)$

  d. $9 \cdot 1 = 9$
  e. none of these

_____c_____ 5. Evaluate $3x − 7y^2$ when $x = −5$ and $y = 2$.
  a. −13
  b. −29
  c. −43

  d. −420
  e. none of these

_____b_____ 6. Solve $2x − 9 = 4(x − 3) + 19$.
  a. −20
  b. −8
  c. $−\dfrac{31}{2}$

  d. 1
  e. none of these

_____b_____ 7. Solve $3y + 7 = 64$.
  a. $\dfrac{71}{3}$
  b. 19
  c. $\dfrac{43}{3}$

  d. 213
  e. none of these

_____d_____ 8. The sum of 16 and five times a number is at least 1. Which of the following numbers is in the solution set?
  a. −7
  b. −5
  c. −6

  d. −3
  e. none of these

_____a_____ 9. Find the LCM of 28, 6, and 32.
    a. 672   d. 224
    b. 2   e. none of these
    c. 84

_____e_____ 10. Write 35 in base 4.
    a. 41_4 d. 213_4
    b. 223_4 e. none of these
    c. 82_4

_____c_____ 11. Write 100111_2 in base 10.
    a. 19   d. 30
    b. 24   e. none of these
    c. 39

_____c_____ 12. Convert $\frac{7}{10}$ to a decimal.
    a. 0.07   d. 70
    b. 7   e. none of these
    c. 0.7

_____e_____ 13. Convert 6.18 to rational form.
    a. $6\frac{18}{10}$ d. $\frac{609}{100}$
    b. $6\frac{1}{50}$ e. none of these
    c. $6\frac{9}{500}$

_____d_____ 14. Convert $0.\overline{45}$ to rational form.
    a. $\frac{4}{9}$ d. $\frac{5}{11}$
    b. $\frac{6}{13}$ e. none of these
    c. $\frac{45}{100}$

_____c_____ 15. Compare $\frac{5}{13}$ and $\frac{3}{7}$ and choose the correct symbol.
    a. >   d. =
    b. ≥   e. none of these
    c. <

7 Percents

Visualizing Percent (Enrichment; use after 7.1.)

Students will need graph paper and colored pencils for this activity.

A pictorial representation of percent can be made using a 10×10 unit grid. The entire grid represents one whole, or 100%. Thus, 80% is represented as shown below.

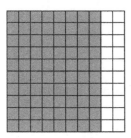

Determine the percent illustrated by each diagram.

____25%____ 1.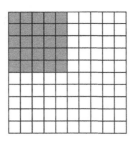

____10%____ 2.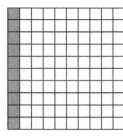

____5%____ 3.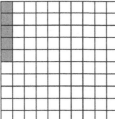

____65.5%____ 4.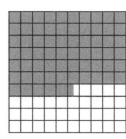

____145%____ 5.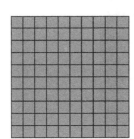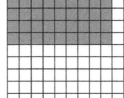

Solving Basic Percent Equations (Extra Practice; use after 7.2.)

Solve by using the formula, percent × whole = part.

_____24_____ 1. What is 6% of 400?

_____25_____ 2. What number is 20% of 125?

_____20%_____ 3. 16 is what percent of 80?

_____140_____ 4. 15% of what number is 21?

_____25%_____ 5. What percent of 84 is 21?

_____50_____ 6. 18% of what number is 9?

_____45%_____ 7. 27 is what percent of 60?

_____75_____ 8. 4.5 is 6% of what number?

_____204_____ 9. What is 300% of 68?

_____30_____ 10. 12% of what number is 3.6?

_____300%_____ 11. 39 is what percent of 13?

_____0.86_____ 12. What is 0.4% of 215?

Solve by using a proportion, $\frac{\text{part}}{\text{whole}} = \frac{\text{percent}}{100}$.

_____11.1_____ 13. 15% of 74 is what number?

_____5%_____ 14. 7 is what percent of 140?

_____60%_____ 15. 24 is what percent of 40?

_____240_____ 16. $\frac{3}{8}$% of what number is $\frac{9}{10}$?

_____72_____ 17. 9 is 12.5% of what number?

_____70_____ 18. 15% of what number is 10.5?

_____400%_____ 19. 512 is what percent of 128?

_____512_____ 20. What is $\frac{1}{3}$% of 153,600?

Complete the table by filling in the missing values. Reduce fractions to lowest terms.

	Fraction	Decimal	Percent
21.	$\frac{1}{4}$	0.25	25%
22.	$\frac{1}{20}$	0.05	5%
23.	$\frac{13}{20}$	0.65	65%
24.	$\frac{7}{16}$	0.4375	43.75%
25.	$\frac{2}{3}$	$0.\overline{6}$	$66\frac{2}{3}$%
26.	$\frac{18}{25}$	0.72	72%

Creation Wonders—The Bat (Bible Activity; use after 7.3.)

The curse of sin brought to the earth the ravishes of millions of insects, but God in His kindness provided a most unusual and effective creature to control these pests. The bat is one of the smallest mammals and the only one that can fly. The majority of bats are insect eaters, having enormous appetites. A single bat can eat over 1,000 insects per hour. It has been estimated that the 20 million or so in the Mexican free-tailed bat colony inhabiting Bracken Cave near San Antonio, Texas, consume from 200 to 250 tn. of insects in a single night. To do this, they must scatter over thousands of square miles during the night.

People, out of ignorance, have developed many false ideas about bats. The majority of bats can see quite well and can hear even better. In fact, their sensitive hearing plays a significant role in nighttime navigation. The Creator has designed them with a sonar navigation system called echolocation. Bat wings are like large hands with skin stretched between the fingers. Bats use their wings to catch insects, and they can grasp because they have a thumb. Bats can fly swiftly with great maneuverability resembling acrobatics, yet they never run into objects in the dark. Contrary to superstition, they do not get caught in people's hair or suck human blood, but they do sleep upside down, and many hibernate during the winter. Some bats are extremely small—only an inch long with a three-inch wingspan—while larger bats may have a wingspan of over 6 ft.

1. Three verses in the Bible mention bats: Leviticus 11:19; Deuteronomy 14:18; and Isaiah 2:20. Read Isaiah 2:19–21. According to these verses, where do bats live?
   in caves and clefts of the rocks

2. If 20 million Mexican free-tailed bats consume 250 tn. of insects in a single night, what is the average weight in ounces of insects consumed per bat?
   0.4 oz.

3. The Mexican free-tailed bat weighs about 0.5 oz. What percent of its body weight does it eat in insects each night?
   80%

4. Bats can fly more than 60 mi./hr. over a vast area searching for insects. How far can a bat travel from its cave dwelling during 8 hr. of nighttime foraging, assuming it flies back to its cave by the same route?
   240 mi.

5. Considering that a blue whale weighs 150 tn. and a Mexican free-tailed bat weighs 0.5 oz., the weight of 20 million bats equals that of how many blue whales?
   about two blue whales

Thou art the God that doest wonders: thou hast declared thy strength among the people.
Psalm 77:14

Scale Drawings (Enhanced Practice; use after 7.4.)

Students will need a ruler and a tape measure for this activity.

Make a scale drawing of the rooms in your home. Include your scale. Be sure to include locations of windows, doors, and closets.

Problem Solving—Percents   (Use after 7.6.)

Specify what the variable stands for, write an equation, and solve. Write remainders as fractions or as decimals rounded to the nearest hundredth.

1. The tourist information center states that the northern half of the state is sunny 65% of the time. How many days during the year can the residents expect cloudy conditions?
   128 days

2. A local discount store's weekend sales increased 25%. If the store's normal weekend sales were $52,800, what are the sales now?
   $66,000

3. In just one day a flower shop sold 45 dozen roses from its stock of 65 dozen. What percent of the rose inventory was sold?
   69.23%

4. A printer needs to increase his production by at least 30% to meet his obligations. If his current output is 135,000 pages/day, what level of output does he need to reach?
   175,500 pages/day

5. If 75% of the youth group voted to go to Carowinds and the other 12 teens voted to go to Kings Dominion, how many are in the youth group?
   48 teens

6. The girls are baking 16 dozen cookies for a big outreach event. If they baked 90 cookies in the morning, what percent of the task will need to be completed during the afternoon?
   53.13%

7. The Sneaker Shop, Ltd. has running shoes on sale for $96 per pair at its 20% off sale. What was the original price of the shoes?
   $120

8. Raphael earns a 20% commission on all registered dogs that he sells. What did he earn if he sold $8,000 worth of registered dogs last month?
   $1,600

9. After-Christmas sales are often a series of discounts that get larger and larger. If a company has successive sales of 15% off, 20% off, 25% off, and 30% off, what percent discount does a customer realize when buying during the fourth sale?
   64.3%

10. An architect's drawing paper is 560 mm × 860 mm. The scale that he uses is 20 mm : 1 m. Is he able to draw a 25 m × 40 m floor plan on the paper if there needs to be an 8 mm margin around the floor plan? What are the required dimensions for the drawing, including the border?
    yes; 516 mm × 816 mm

Graduated Commission (Enhanced Practice; use after 7.6.)

Some companies pay their employees by a graduated commission. For example, Jessica works at a computer store and earns money each week by a combination of fixed salary and graduated commission. Each week she is guaranteed to earn $100 plus the following graduated commission on her total sales for the week.

Sales	Commission
up to $4,000	12%
over $4,000 and up to $10,000	15%
over $10,000	17%

This means that on the first $4,000 of sales Jessica earns 12% commission, and on those sales between $4,000 and $10,000 she earns 15% commission. Then for any sales above $10,000 she earns 17% on the portion greater than $10,000.

Example

Jessica sells $16,000 of computer equipment one week. How much does she earn that week?

Answer

Jessica is guaranteed $100 each week.

She earns 12% on the first $4,000: 0.12(4,000) = $480.

On the next $6,000 that she sold, she earns 15%: 0.15(6,000) = $900.

This accounts for the first $10,000 of sales. But she sold $6,000 beyond $10,000. She earns 17% on this last $6,000: 0.17(6,000) = $1,020.

Adding up all of these amounts produces Jessica's total income for the week.

100 + 480 + 900 + 1,020 = $2,500; Jessica earned $2,500 this week.

Calculate Jessica's weekly income if she sells the following total amounts each week.

_____$460_____ 1. $3,000

_____$1,180_____ 2. $8,000

_____$737.50_____ 3. $5,050

_____$1,905_____ 4. $12,500

Looking back at the example, follow the steps below to determine Jessica's income for the week. Place the answer for each step on the line provided.

_____$1,920_____ 5. Calculate the base (lowest) commission rate on the entire $16,000.

_____$180_____ 6. Calculate the extra 3% commission earned on sales between $4,000 and $10,000.

_____$300_____ 7. Calculate the extra 5% commission earned on sales over $10,000.

_____$2,500_____ 8. Including the $100 guaranteed weekly salary, find Jessica's total weekly income.

_____yes_____ 9. Does the answer to exercise 8 equal the answer calculated in the example?

10. Why do these two methods produce the same result?
    Answers may vary. For either method, the first $4,000 is multiplied by only 12%. The next $6,000 is multiplied by 15%, or 12% + 3% = 15%. The rest of the sales is multiplied by 17%, or 12% + 5% = 17%.

Calculator Skill 7 (Use after 7.7.)

written for the TI-30Xa

Compound Interest Applications

With compound interest the growth of the investment is based on how much money one has rather than how much he started with: interest earned at each point in time also earns interest in the next period of time. Ben Franklin understood the power of compound interest when he left 1,000 pounds sterling to each of the cities of Boston and Philadelphia. He made stipulations about how it was to be invested and what the money was to be used for. His money, which has grown to millions of dollars, significantly advanced the cause of education in those two cities.

You have learned that at each compounding point the previous principal P earns interest at rate i. This means that the amount of money after one compounding period is $S = P + iP = P(1 + i)$. After two periods it is $S = P(1 + i)^2$, and after n periods it is $S = P(1 + i)^n$. Thus, $(1 + i)^n$ is called the *interest rate factor*.

In the simple interest formula, $I = Prt$, r = the annual interest rate and t = the time in years. In the compound interest formula, n = the number of compounding periods and i = the interest rate per compounding period. Therefore, $i = r \div n$, or the annual rate divided by the number of compounding periods per year. When interest is compounded annually, $n = t$ and $i = r$.

Example 1

How much is \$4,570 worth in 100 yr. if it is invested at 5% compounded annually?

Answer

$S = 4,570(1 + 0.05)^{100}$

Keystrokes: $\boxed{(}$ 1 $\boxed{+}$ $\boxed{.}$ 05 $\boxed{)}$ $\boxed{y^x}$ 100 $\boxed{=}$ $\boxed{\times}$ 4570 $\boxed{=}$. Result: \$600,960.75.

Example 2

How much is \$1,000 worth in 25 yr. if it is invested at 6% compounded quarterly?

Answer

Calculate the rate per quarter: $0.06 \div 4 = 0.015$. The number of quarters in 25 yr. is $4 \times 25 = 100$.

$S = 1,000(1 + 0.015)^{100}$

Keystrokes: $\boxed{(}$ 1 $\boxed{+}$ $\boxed{.}$ 015 $\boxed{)}$ $\boxed{y^x}$ 100 $\boxed{=}$ $\boxed{\times}$ 1000 $\boxed{=}$. Result: \$4,432.05.

Another form of the compound interest formula is $P = \dfrac{S}{(1 + i)^n}$. Use this formula to find the principal needed to insure a desired return on an investment.

Example 3

How much should a father invest to obtain at least \$20,000 in his child's college fund at the end of twelve years? He has access to an investment that pays 7% compounded monthly.

Answer

compounding periods: $n = 12(12) = 144$; interest rate: $i = \dfrac{0.07}{12}$

Use $P = \dfrac{S}{(1 + i)^n}$, and substitute the known values: $P = \dfrac{20,000}{\left(1 + \dfrac{0.07}{12}\right)^{144}}$.

Keystrokes: $\boxed{(}$ $\boxed{.}$ 07 $\boxed{\div}$ 12 $\boxed{+}$ 1 $\boxed{)}$ $\boxed{y^x}$ 144 $\boxed{=}$ $\boxed{1/x}$ $\boxed{\times}$ 20000 $\boxed{=}$. Result: \$8,655.31.

Notice that we calculated the denominator first and then used the reciprocal button (see Calculator Skill 2). We could have stored the result of the denominator in memory, entered 20,000, and then divided by recalling the denominator from storage.

Find the number of compounding periods and the interest rate factor, given the annual interest rate, compounding period, and time.

	Annual Interest Rate	Compounding Period	Time	Number of Compounding Periods, n	Interest Rate Factor $(1 + i)^n$
1.	6%	semiannually	5 yr.	10	1.343916379
2.	7.5%	quarterly	30 mo.	10	1.204137877
3.	8%	monthly	30 yr.	360	10.93572967
4.	12%	quarterly	15 yr.	60	5.891603104

Solve the following compound interest problems.

5. Find the value after 5 yr. for $10,000 invested at 6% compounded semiannually.
   $13,439.16

6. Find the amount after 30 yr. of an $18,000 deposit in a mutual fund paying 8% compounded monthly.
   $196,843.13

7. An inheritance is invested for a three-year-old in a college education stock fund averaging 12% compounded quarterly. What sum should be invested if the anticipated college costs at eighteen years old are $80,000?
   $13,578.65

8. On May 25, 2010, Andy invested the $4,000 he received from the sale of some rare baseball cards. If the investment earns 5% compounded quarterly, how much is in his account on August 25, 2013?
   $4,701.06

9. A South Trust bank borrowed $3,200,000 from the Federal Reserve Bank to meet its reserve requirements. If the Fed charges member banks 3% compounded daily and the loan was repaid in 27 days, how much interest did South Trust pay?
   $7,108.96

10. When twelve-year old Rachel won $1,000 in a contest, her dad convinced her to invest it in a Roth IRA mutual fund that pays an average of 9% compounded quarterly. If she does not add any more money, how much will her fund be worth when she is 67?
   $133,637.91

11. How much should you invest at age 12 in order to have $12,000 when you are 18? Assume that your savings institution pays 5% compounded quarterly.
   $8,906.36

12. How much should your parents have invested when you were born in order to have $25,000 when you are 22? Assume that your parents earned 6% compounded quarterly.
   $6,744.17

13. Suppose your grandfather invested $1,000 when your father was born for his college education. Assume the fund paid 5% compounded annually. However, your father won a scholarship to college and kept the money in the college fund for you. If your father is thirty years older than you, how much will be in the fund when you are 18?
   $10,401.27

14. If Brandon invests his inheritance of $150,000 in a fund paying 7% compounded monthly, how long will it take before the fund doubles to at least $300,000? (Hint: Since you do not have a formula for the number of interest periods n, use a guess-and-check problem-solving method.)
   10 yr.

Chapter 7 Review

Write T for true or F for false. If the statement is false, correct it or give an example showing why it is false.

_____T_____ 1. A percent must be changed to a decimal or a fraction before it is multiplied or divided.

_____T_____ 2. A percent is a ratio comparing a number to one hundred.

_____F_____ 3. If the discount rate is 15%, you multiply the retail price by 15% to get the sale price.
Change "sale price" to "discount."

_____F_____ 4. When you take a percent of a number, your answer is always smaller than the original number.
Counterexample: 200% of 10 is 20.

_____F_____ 5. A commission is the amount you save on an item.
Change "commission" to "discount."

Write each percent as a fraction.

___$\frac{16}{25}$___ 6. 64%

___$2\frac{9}{20}$___ 7. 245%

Write each as a percent.

___60%___ 8. $\frac{3}{5}$

___40%___ 9. 0.4

Write each percent as a decimal.

___3.14___ 10. 314%

___0.32___ 11. 32%

Solve. Write remainders as fractions.

___$12\frac{1}{2}\%$___ 12. 15 is what percent of 120?

___5___ 13. What is 4% of 125?

___310___ 14. 20% of what number is 62?

___$66\frac{2}{3}\%$___ 15. What percent of 51 is 34?

16. The junior class is pricing class rings. They were told that the price of 10 karat gold is 80% that of 14 karat gold. If the price of a 10 karat gold ring is $165, what is the price of an identical 14 karat gold ring?
$206.25

17. Jim missed one of the 65 questions on the Bible test. What is his test score to the nearest percent?
98%

18. If Jeremiah buys a baseball glove for $44.99 and the sales tax is 6%, how much must he pay for the glove?
$47.69

Find the distance if the scale is 3 cm : 5 mi.

_____30 mi._____ 19. 18 cm

_____$41\frac{2}{3}$ mi._____ 20. 25 cm

Find the discount and sale price for the following items. If necessary, round to the nearest cent.

_____$5.90; $23.60_____ 21. retail price: $29.50; discount rate: 20%

_____$15.20; $22.80_____ 22. retail price: $38.00; discount rate: 40%

Find the markup and retail price for the following items. If necessary, round to the nearest cent.

_____$26.03; $94.53_____ 23. cost: $68.50; markup rate: 38%

_____$0.18; $1.47_____ 24. cost: $1.29; markup rate: 14%

Find the earnings for the following sales and commissions. If necessary, round to the nearest cent.

_____$14.76_____ 25. sales: $246; commission: 6%

_____$164.18_____ 26. sales: $2,189; commission: 7.5%

Find the simple interest earned and the total amount in the following investment accounts.

_____$198; $1,098_____ 27. $900 invested at 11% for 2 yr.

_____$46.88; $1,296.88_____ 28. $1,250 invested at 9% for 5 mo.

Find the percent change. Indicate whether it is an increase or a decrease.

_____75% increase_____ 29. original amount: 20; new amount: 35

_____21.4% decrease_____ 30. original amount: 70; new amount: 55

Cumulative Review 7

<u>d</u>   1. Which of the following numbers is not a rational number?

     a. $\frac{5}{4}$ d. $\sqrt{7}$

     b. -9 e. none of these

     c. $0.\overline{21}$

<u>a</u>   2. The sum of 8 and five times a number is -22. Find the number.

     a. -6 d. $-\frac{1}{6}$

     b. $\frac{14}{5}$ e. none of these

     c. -5

<u>c</u>   3. 29 less than the quotient of a number and 4 is -21. Which of the following equations could be used to solve this problem?

     a. $29 - \frac{n}{4} = -21$ d. $\frac{n}{4} - 21 = -29$

     b. $29 < \frac{n}{4} - 21$ e. none of these

     c. $\frac{n}{4} - 29 = -21$

<u>b</u>   4. Find the GCF of 165 and 735.

     a. 3   d. 5

     b. 15   e. none of these

     c. 35

<u>e</u>   5. Write the first three terms in the sequence defined by $a_n = 7n - 4$.

     a. $-4, 3, 10$ d. $-11, -18, -25$

     b. $1, 2, 3$ e. none of these

     c. $3, 10, 18$

<u>c</u>   6. Add $231_4 + 332_4$.

     a. 563_4 d. 1333_4

     b. 2333_4 e. none of these

     c. 1223_4

<u>a</u>   7. Subtract $10011_2 - 111_2$.

     a. 1100_2 d. 1010_2

     b. 11000_2 e. none of these

     c. 10100_2

<u>a</u>   8. Convert $\frac{7}{8}$ to a decimal.

     a. 0.875   d. 0.675

     b. 1.143   e. none of these

     c. 0.778

_____b_____ 9. Solve $\frac{x}{9} = \frac{24}{36}$.

        a. 8   d. 22.9

        b. 6   e. none of these

        c. 81

_____d_____ 10. Solve $\frac{n+9}{8} = \frac{10}{16}$.

        a. $\frac{89}{16}$ d. -4

                                                e. none of these

        b. $\frac{71}{16}$

        c. 14

_____e_____ 11. If a dragster travels the quarter-mile track in record time, it will cross the finish line at about 484 ft./sec. How fast is the car traveling at the finish line in miles per hour?

        a. 300 mi./hr.   d. 275 mi./hr.

        b. 158 mi./hr.   e. none of these

        c. 533.5 mi./hr.

_____b_____ 12. Add $\frac{4}{15} + \frac{7}{35}$.

        a. $\frac{14}{25}$ d. $\frac{11}{15}$

        b. $\frac{7}{15}$ e. none of these

        c. $\frac{11}{105}$

_____b_____ 13. Simplify $-0.63(128.7)$.

        a. 128.07   d. -129.33

        b. -81.081 e. none of these

        c. -0.0049

_____a_____ 14. Simplify $18x^2 + 2xy - 3y^2 - 4xy + 12x^2$.

        a. $30x^2 - 2xy - 3y^2$ d. $6x^2 - 2xy - 3y^2$

        b. $30x^2 + 6xy - 3y^2$ e. none of these

        c. $27x^2 - 2xy$

_____d_____ 15. Simplify $-7(x + 2) - 6(3x - 1)$.

        a. $-25x + 20$ d. $-25x - 8$

        b. $-25x + 1$ e. none of these

        c. $-25x - 20$

8 Applying Equations and Inequalities

Creation Wonders—The Human Cell (Bible Activity; use after 8.1.)

Of all God's creation, nothing is as marvelous as humans. We are more than just animals because we are created in the image of God. We can think, reason, create, and communicate abstract ideas such as love and hate. Besides this vast spectrum of the mind and soul, the human body is overwhelming in its intricate complexity. King David expressed his amazement in Psalm 139:14—"I will praise thee; for I am fearfully and wonderfully made: marvelous are thy works; and that my soul knoweth right well."

Although David knew about his heart and lungs, he probably did not realize that his heart beat about 100,000 times a day and his lungs processed about 10,000 L of air a day. The technology of our age lets us investigate the most complex and microscopic systems of the human body. Such studies reveal that our bodies are composed of about 100 trillion cells (10^{14}). The average size of a cell is about 40 micrometers (abbreviated as μm; 1 μm is one-millionth of a meter). Even though cells have similar components, cells for various parts and functions of the body vary significantly in size, shape, and function. Red blood cells transport oxygen, nerve cells transmit information, glandular cells secrete hormones, and muscle cells control body movements. Yet all these cells are built from the same material and have the same DNA. Some scientists claim that the human cell is the most complex entity in the universe.

1. To help you understand the immensity of the number of cells in the human body, suppose you count at a rate of 1 cell per second nonstop day and night until you reach 10^{14}. How long in years is 10^{14} sec.?
   3,170,979 ≈ 3 million yr.

2. Suppose you connect the cells in the human body in a long chain. How many times would this chain reach around the earth? Use 40 μm for the average size of a cell and 40,075.16 km for the circumference of the earth.
   99.812 ≈ 100 times around the earth

3. If the human heart beats on average seventy times per minute, how many times will it beat over a seventy-year span?
   2,575,440,000 ≈ 2.6 billion times

4. If our lungs process 10,000 L a day and a liter is defined as a cube measuring 1 dm on a side, how large of a cube is a day's worth of air? Give the dimensions in meters.
   10 m³, or a cube measuring 2.15 m on each side

5. If the smallest cells have a diameter of 7 μm and the largest have a diameter of 120 μm, how do their volumes compare, assuming they are spherical? (Volume of a sphere = $\frac{4}{3}\pi r^3$; let $\pi = 3.14159$.)
   179.59 μm³; 904,777.92 μm³; The larger cells have more than 5,000 times the volume of the smaller ones.

> *So God created man in his own image, in the image of God created he him; male and female created he them. . . . And God saw every thing that he had made, and, behold, it was very good. And the evening and the morning were the sixth day.* Genesis 1:27, 31

Simplifying—Variables on Two Sides (Extra Practice; use after 8.2.)

Solve the following equations by simplifying first.

_____2_____ 1. $12x - 19 = 2x + 1$

_____-4_____ 2. $4y + 21 = -2y - 3$

_____54_____ 3. $8(z - 12) = 3(2z + 4)$

_____$\frac{18}{7}$_____ 4. $18a - 13 + 2a = 6a + 23$

_____-3_____ 5. $13b = 2(3b - 12) + 3$

_____$\frac{5}{4}$_____ 6. $-6(3c + 5) + 3c + 5 = c - 45$

_____2_____ 7. $1.5(4w + 1) - 7.5 = 2.5w + 1$

_____-1_____ 8. $21x - 63 = 2(14x - 31) + 6$

_____$-\frac{5}{2}$_____ 9. $\frac{2}{3}x + \frac{5}{12} = \frac{1}{6}x - \frac{5}{6}$

_____$-\frac{7}{5}$_____ 10. $\frac{1}{2}\left(\frac{3}{4}y - \frac{1}{4}\right) = \frac{1}{6}y - \frac{5}{12}$

_____53_____ 11. $21z - 3(2z + 14) = 14z + 11$

_____2_____ 12. $16(5 - 3w) = 2(3w - 14)$

_____-2_____ 13. $5.25a - 2(3a + 1.25) = a + 1$

_____$-\frac{15}{8}$_____ 14. $2b + 3 + 4b + 5 = 6b - 7 - 8b$

_____$\frac{1}{2}$_____ 15. $50(2 - 0.5c) - 70 = 20 - 5c$

_____-9_____ 16. $4(3x + 12 - x + 2) = 2x + 2$

_____1_____ 17. $10^3y - 460 = 3(10^2y + 80)$

_____1_____ 18. $0.004(2z + 8) = 0.05z - 0.01$

_____13_____ 19. $\frac{4}{5}x - \frac{1}{20} = \frac{3}{4}x + \frac{3}{5}$

_____-12_____ 20. $\frac{5}{16}x = \frac{1}{3}\left(\frac{3}{4}x - \frac{9}{4}\right)$

Equation Versus Identity (Enhanced Practice; use after 8.2.)

A mathematical equation and a mathematical identity look very similar. $2x + 7 = x + 9$ is an equation, whereas $x + 7 = 7 + x$ is an identity. Equations have a finite (fixed) number of solutions, but identities have an infinite number of solutions. In fact, the solution for an identity is all real numbers.

Example 1

Solve $2x + 7 = x + 9$.

Answer

$$2x + 7 = x + 9$$
$$2x + 7 - x = x + 9 - x \qquad \text{1. Subtract } x \text{ from both sides.}$$
$$x + 7 - 7 = 9 - 7 \qquad \text{2. Subtract 7 from both sides.}$$
$$x = 2 \qquad \text{3. Simplify.}$$

This is an equation since it has one solution that makes it true, namely $x = 2$.

Example 2

Solve $x + 7 = 7 + x$.

Answer

$$x + 7 = 7 + x$$
$$x + 7 - x = 7 + x - x \qquad \text{1. Subtract } x \text{ from both sides.}$$
$$7 - 7 = 7 - 7 \qquad \text{2. Subtract 7 from both sides.}$$
$$0 = 0 \qquad \text{3. Simplify.}$$

This is an identity since it has an infinite number of solutions. Every real number makes this equation true. Notice that when you solve an identity, the variable disappears and the result is a true statement, such as $0 = 0$.

Solve to determine whether each statement is an equation or an identity. If the statement is an identity, write the answer as $\mathbb{R}$. If the statement is an equation, find the solution.

_____$\mathbb{R}$_____ 1. $2(x + 6) + 5 = 3x - x + 17$ _____$\mathbb{R}$_____ 2. $x + 8 = 8 + x$

_____-4_____ 3. $6x + 9 = 2x - 7$ _____$\mathbb{R}$_____ 4. $-4(x + 2) = 8x - 8 - 12x$

_____ℝ_____ 5. $(3 + x) + 6 = 3 + (x + 6)$ _____$\frac{1}{2}$_____ 6. $-12x + 9 = 8x - 3 + 4x$

_____0_____ 7. $x + 9 = 9 + 2x$ _____ℝ_____ 8. $3x + 9 = 6 + (3 - 4x) + 7x$

_____−2_____ 9. $5x + 12 = -x$ _____ℝ_____ 10. $12 - 4x = 2(6 - 2x)$

11. Which real number property is illustrated in exercise 2? Is it an identity?
    Commutative Property of Addition; yes

12. Which real number property is illustrated in exercise 5? Is it an identity?
    Associative Property of Addition; yes

13. Are the properties of real numbers always identities?
    yes, with the exception that zero must be excluded for the Inverse Property of Multiplication

Calculator Skill 8 (Use after 8.2.)

written for the TI-30Xa

Solution of Equations and Applications

In this chapter you are working on equations requiring several steps to solve. Many of these equations have constants on both sides and variables on both sides. As you saw in Chapter 3, the calculator can be a great tool for helping you solve real-life equations in which the numbers are often decimals or fractions. Calculators let you avoid tedious arithmetic as you solve problems.

Example 1

Solve $120.345x - 345.824 = 194.785$.

Answer

$120.345x - 345.824 = 194.785$

$\qquad 120.345x = 540.609 \qquad$ 1. Add 345.824 to both sides.

$\qquad\qquad x = 4.49216004 \qquad$ 2. Divide both sides by 120.345, the coefficient of the variable.

Example 2

Solve $3\frac{1}{8} + 2\frac{4}{5}x - 1\frac{1}{2}x = 5\frac{3}{4}$.

Answer

$3\frac{1}{8} + 2\frac{4}{5}x - 1\frac{1}{2}x = 5\frac{3}{4}$

$\qquad 2\frac{4}{5}x - 1\frac{1}{2}x = 2\frac{5}{8} \qquad$ 1. Use the $\boxed{A^b/c}$ key to subtract $3\frac{1}{8}$ from $5\frac{3}{4}$.

$\qquad\qquad 1\frac{3}{10}x = 2\frac{5}{8} \qquad$ 2. Using the $\boxed{A^b/c}$ key, subtract to combine like terms on the left side of the equation.

$\qquad\qquad\qquad x = 2\frac{1}{52} \qquad$ 3. Use the $\boxed{A^b/c}$ key to divide $2\frac{5}{8}$ by $1\frac{3}{10}$, the coefficient of x.

Use a calculator to solve the following equations.

$\underline{\qquad x \approx 0.855957 \qquad}$ 1. $85.1356 + 24.215x = 105.8626$

$\underline{\qquad x = -0.5 \qquad}$ 2. $515x - 283 = 265x - 408$

$\underline{\qquad x \approx 2.305882 \qquad}$ 3. $2{,}565 - 425x = 1{,}585$

$\underline{\qquad x \approx 52.7619 \qquad}$ 4. $0.025x + 1.028 = 0.004x + 2.136$

$\underline{\qquad x = 22\frac{70}{297} \qquad}$ 5. $\frac{56}{65}x + 3\frac{1}{5} = \frac{21}{12}x - 16\frac{5}{9}$

Use a calculator to determine whether the value given for x is a solution to the equation. If not, give the correct solution.

_____ no; $x = -139.\overline{09}$ _____ 6. $78x - 216 = 23(x - 342)$; $x = -102$

_____ yes _____ 7. $22{,}950 = 50x + 16{,}640$; $x = 126.2$

_____ no; $x = 180.375$ _____ 8. $0.25x - 15.625 = 20.45 + 0.05x$; $x = 24$

_____ yes _____ 9. $(3 \times 10^4)x + (1.5 \times 10^5) = 4.5 \times 10^5$; $x = 10$

_____ no; $x = -8\frac{21}{38}$ _____ 10. $22\frac{3}{5}x + 6\frac{2}{25} = 25\frac{16}{25}x + 32\frac{2}{25}$; $x = 8\frac{21}{38}$

Art and Design (Enrichment; use after 8.3.)

Students will need graph paper and colored pencils for this activity.

The orderliness of mathematics serves well as a means of generating designs with aesthetic beauty. The ways numerical values can be used to display visual schemes strains the imagination.

Because of its simplicity, a mod 5 multiplication table of nonzero values is used to generate a design. (Modular arithmetic is discussed in the Dominion thru Math exercises in Section 4.1.)

Begin by making a mod 5 multiplication table. The four nonzero mod 5 digits are arranged nonsequentially in the headers of the table below, and then they are multiplied by each other to fill in the table. Changing the order of the digits would allow you to create a different design.

×	1	3	4	2
1	1	3	4	2
3	3	4	2	1
4	4	2	1	3
2	2	1	3	4

After making the table, assign a small block design in a four-chamber grid to each of the four digits.

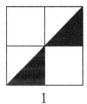

1

2

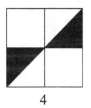

3   4

1. Draw the block designs on graph paper, in the arrangment indicated by the numbers in the mod 5 multiplication table, to create an 8 × 8 array.
   See answer diagram on the next page.

2. Reflect the design in exercise 1 across its right edge to create an 8 × 16 array.
   See answer diagram on the next page.

3. Finally, reflect the design in exercise 2 across its bottom edge to create a 16 × 16 array for the completed design.
   See answer diagram on the next page.

4. Generate a different design by making a new mod 5 multiplication table with the factors arranged differently. Use the same numbered block designs you used for exercises 1–3.
   Answers will vary.

5. Create four different block designs of your own. They should each be in a four-chamber grid like the ones you used for exercises 1–4, but create your own simple patterns. Use the mod 5 multiplication table you made in exercise 4 and your new designs to make a 16 × 16 design.
   Answers will vary.

1.

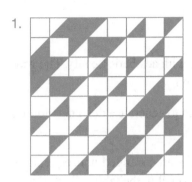

2.

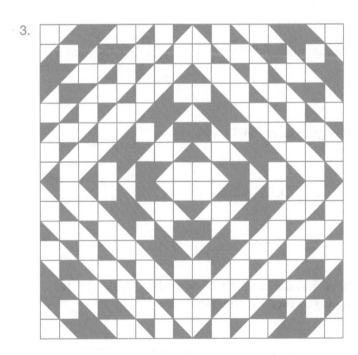

3.

Note: Consider using interactive geometry software to complete this activity.

Problem Solving—Equations and Inequalities (Use after 8.5.)

Follow the four-step problem-solving strategy to solve the following problems. For most you will need to write an equation or an inequality using the variable you select to represent the unknown.

1. A long-jump competitor's best jump of 20 ft. 6 in. is 6 in. short of doubling the length of his personal worst jump as a beginner. What was his personal worst jump?

   $2x = 20.5 + 0.5; x = 10.5$ ft.

2. At a swim meet, the scores of three judges are added and then multiplied by the degree of difficulty of the dive. Chong made a dive with a 2.8 degree of difficulty, and two of the judges' scores were 9.5 and 8.5. If his total score was 75.88, what score did the third judge give him?

   $2.8(9.5 + 8.5 + x) = 75.88; x = 9.1$

3. Another contestant at the swim meet scored 56.75 with scores from the judges of 7.5, 8.0, and 7.2. What was the degree of difficulty for that contestant's dive?

   $x(7.5 + 8.0 + 7.2) = 56.75; x = 2.5$

4. Find three consecutive even numbers such that twelve times the smallest equals ten times the largest.

   $12n = 10(n + 4);$ 20, 22, and 24

5. Donna has finished reading 80% of *War and Peace* and has 268 pages left to read. How many pages has she read?

   x = the total number of pages; $x = 0.8x + 268; x = 1,340$; pages read = 1,072

6. Mr. Standrich has to drive 416 mi. to a meeting. What speed must he average in order to get there in no more than 6.5 hr.?

   $6.5r \geq 416; r \geq 64$ mi./hr.

7. Edmond invested $1,000 in a fund that pays 7% compounded quarterly. After how many quarters will he have at least $2,000?

   $1,000(1 + 0.0175)^n \geq 2,000; n \geq 40$ quarters (10 yr.)

8. Anna Kay has test scores of 83%, 91%, 89%, and 90% with one test remaining. What does she need to score on that last test to earn at least a 90% average?

$\frac{83 + 91 + 89 + 90 + x}{5} \geq 90; x \geq 97\%$

9. Anita is expecting at least 125 people for the church supper. If she allows half a liter of lemonade per person, what is the minimum amount of lemonade she should make?

$x \geq 125(0.5); x \geq 62.5$ L

10. A school recycles 26 tn. of paper each month. The amount of newsprint is 2 tn. short of three times as much as all the rest of the paper. How much newsprint and how much other paper is recycled?

$(3x - 2) + x = 26; x = 7$ tn. of other paper and 19 tn. of newsprint

11. On the moon a person weighs only $\frac{1}{6}$ of his weight on the earth (due to the smaller size of the moon and the lesser force of gravity). If the sum of Omar's moon weight and earth weight is 210 lb., how much does he weigh on the earth?

$w + \frac{1}{6}w = 210; w = 180$ lb.

12. The exterior of a house is being painted with paint that has a stated coverage rate of 270 to 400 ft.²/gal. If the exterior is 2,430 ft.², excluding windows, give an inequality showing the range of gallons of paint needed.

$\frac{2,430}{400} \leq x \leq \frac{2,430}{270}; 6.075$ gal. $\leq x \leq 9$ gal.

13. Nancy has only $20 to purchase a meal at a restaurant. If she knows the tax is 8% and she plans to leave a 15% tip, what is the maximum price she can pay for a meal? (Assume that she tips on the total after the tax is added.)

$1.08x + 0.15(1.08x) \leq 20; x \leq \$16.10$

Chapter 8 Review

Simplify.

_____$-2x + 18y - 21$_____ 1. $5x + 2y - 9 + 16y - 7x - 12$

_____$a + 21$_____ 2. $-3(a - 7) + 4a$

_____$30x^2 + 4x + 30$_____ 3. $10x(3x + 1) - 6(x - 5)$

_____$-9k + 9m - 56$_____ 4. $-9k + 2m + 7(m - 8)$

Solve.

_____$x = -9$_____ 5. $6x - (x + 8) = -53$

_____$x = 6$_____ 6. $2(3x + 4) + 6(x - 8) = 32$

_____$x = \frac{3}{4}$_____ 7. $\frac{1}{2}(4x - 12) + 3x = \frac{-9}{4}$

_____$x = -13$_____ 8. $-7(2x + 8) + 25 = 151$

_____$x = 4$_____ 9. $3x = x + 8$

_____$x = 0$_____ 10. $21(x + 4) - 6x = 2x + 84$

_____$x = 15$_____ 11. $-8(x + 2) - 19 = 3x - 200$

_____$x = -3$_____ 12. $2(x - 7) + 36 = 4(2x - 5) + 60$

_____$x > \frac{3}{4}$_____ 13. $4(x + 3) > 15$

_____$x > 8$_____ 14. $-9(x + 12) < -180$

_____ 15. $\frac{2}{3}y + 5 \leq 17$
$y \leq 18$

_____ 16. $9(3x + 4) + 2(7x - 2) \neq 16$
$x \neq -\frac{16}{41}$

_____ 17. $6.8(9x + 1) = 2.4(3x - 7) + 16$
$x = -0.1\overline{407}$
or $-\frac{19}{135}$

_____ 18. $-5x \geq 4x + 2(6x - 8)$
$x \leq \frac{16}{21}$

Write an equation or inequality for each exercise and solve.

19. The sum of three consecutive integers is –39. Find the integers.
$x + (x + 1) + (x + 2) = -39$; –14, –13, and –12

20. Find three consecutive odd integers such that the sum of twice the smallest and 9 is 10 more than the largest.
$2x + 9 = (x + 4) + 10$; 5, 7, and 9

21. When a plane flies with the wind, it can travel 738 mi. in 3 hr. If the average wind speed is 6 mi./hr., what is the plane's air speed?
$(r + 6)3 = 738$; 240 mi./hr.

22. Jeff and Casson are traveling along a river in a canoe. They are paddling against the current, which is running at 3 mi./hr. If it takes them an hour and a half to paddle upstream 6 mi., how fast could they paddle in still water?
$(r - 3)1.5 = 6$; 7 mi./hr.

23. The difference of four times a number and 18 is not less than 46. Find the range of numbers.
$4x - 18 \geq 46$; $x \geq 16$

24. Asa has $15 that he can spend on school supplies. He needs three notebooks that cost $2.10 each, six pens that cost $0.80 each, and some pencils that cost $0.45 each. If there is a 5% sales tax, how many pencils can he buy?
$1.05[3(2.10) + 6(0.80) + 0.45x] \leq 15$; $x \leq 7.08$; 7 pencils

25. Eli is twice as old as Josh, and Ben is six years older than Josh. The sum of their ages is 50. How old is each person?
$2x + x + (x + 6) = 50$; Eli is 22, Josh is 11, and Ben is 17.

Cumulative Review 8

_____d_____ 1. Write "a number less 8" as an algebraic expression.
  a. $8 - n$
  b. $n < 8$
  c. $8n$
  d. $n - 8$
  e. none of these

_____b_____ 2. Multiply $-2(6)(14)$.
  a. 168
  b. -168
  c. 18
  d. -84
  e. none of these

_____a_____ 3. Simplify $5^3 \cdot 2^2$.
  a. 500
  b. 60
  c. 30
  d. 972
  e. none of these

_____c_____ 4. Give the prime factorization of 14,175.
  a. $3^3 \cdot 5^2 \cdot 7$
  b. $3^4 \cdot 5^2$
  c. $3^4 \cdot 5^2 \cdot 7$
  d. $3^4 \cdot 7$
  e. none of these

_____a_____ 5. What are the next three numbers in the sequence 168, 84, 42, …?
  a. $21, \frac{21}{2}, \frac{21}{4}$
  b. $21, 10, 5$
  c. $21, \frac{21}{2}, \frac{42}{4}$
  d. $21, 7, \frac{7}{3}$
  e. none of these

_____e_____ 6. Write 22 in base 3.
  a. 22_3
  b. 62_3
  c. 1100_3
  d. 210_3
  e. none of these

_____c_____ 7. Which statement about the set of real numbers is false?
  a. $\mathbb{Z} \subseteq \mathbb{Q}$
  b. $\mathbb{Q} \subseteq \mathbb{R}$
  c. $\mathbb{R} \subseteq \mathbb{Q}$
  d. $\mathbb{N} \subseteq \mathbb{Z}$
  e. none of these

_____b_____ 8. Which of the following equations illustrates the Distributive Property?
  a. $a(b + c) = (b + c)a$
  b. $ab + ac = a(b + c)$
  c. $(a + b) + c = a + (b + c)$
  d. $a(b + c) = a(c + b)$
  e. none of these

_____b_____ 9. Which of the following numbers is less than $\frac{7}{8}$?

   a. $\frac{10}{11}$ d. $\frac{21}{23}$

   b. $\frac{4}{5}$ e. none of these

   c. $\frac{15}{17}$

_____c_____ 10. Add $\frac{7}{5} + \frac{2}{9}$.

   a. $1\frac{26}{45}$ d. $\frac{53}{45}$

   b. $\frac{9}{14}$ e. none of these

   c. $\frac{73}{45}$

_____b_____ 11. Divide $\frac{5}{7}$ by $\frac{4}{21}$.

   a. 2   d. $\frac{60}{21}$

   b. $3\frac{3}{4}$ e. none of these

   c. $\frac{20}{147}$

_____d_____ 12. What percent of 150 is 123?

   a. 22%   d. 82%

   b. 122%   e. none of these

   c. 100.86%

_____e_____ 13. Write 14% as a fraction.

   a. $\frac{7}{25}$ d. $\frac{14}{5}$

   b. $\frac{14}{50}$ e. none of these

   c. $\frac{14}{1}$

_____a_____ 14. How much simple interest is earned on a six-year investment of $18,000 at 4%?

   a. $4,320   d. $432,000

   b. $22,320   e. none of these

   c. $720

_____d_____ 15. Find 180% of 2,200.

   a. 39,600   d. 3,960

   b. 396,000   e. none of these

   c. 396

9 Relations and Functions

Creation Wonders—The Human Eye (Bible Activity; use after 9.1.)

Without God's gift of sight we could not experience the glory of God that the heavens proclaim, nor could we relish His handiwork. The human eye, with its complexity, flexibility, and usefulness, makes one of the most dramatic declarations of God's handiwork. With our eyes we can see the beauty of God's creation; but our eyes are also windows into our souls, showing a wide range of emotions. In the Sermon on the Mount, Jesus revealed this truth: "The light of the body is the eye: if therefore thine eye be single, thy whole body shall be full of light. But if thine eye be evil, thy whole body shall be full of darkness" (Matt. 6:22–23a).

Light enters the eye through the pupil, a hole whose diameter is adjusted by the muscles of the iris. In bright light, a smaller-diameter pupil allows less light into the eye; in dim light, a larger-diameter pupil allows more light into the eye. Light is then focused by the lens and is sensed by photoreceptors (special nerve cells) in the retina in the back of the eye. The two types of photoreceptor cells are rods, which sense the presence of light, and cones, which sense the color of light. Each eye has more than 120 million rods and 6 million cones connected by millions of other nerve cells to the brain via the optic nerve. The miniaturization and complexity of this layer of nerve cells far exceed any fiber technology of modern science—one square millimeter of the retina contains as many as 160,000 sensors. The rods also adapt to see not only in the near darkness of night, but also in the bright light of day, requiring a reduction of their sensitivity by 1,000 times. However, the effects of sin have left humans with less than perfect vision, both physically and spiritually.

1. The rods and cones are not evenly distributed in the retina. But based on the total number of rods and cones in the eye and the number of these sensors per square millimeter, what is the area of the retina in square millimeters?
   788 mm²

2. To better understand the size of a sensor, suppose it has a square shape. For 160,000 sensors to occupy 1 mm², what is the size of each sensor?
   6.25×10^{-6} mm²

3. In Isaiah 6, when the prophet saw the Lord "high and lifted up," what effect did the sight have on his person?
   He became extremely aware of his sinfulness and the great holiness of God.

4. An eyewitness is someone who sees something and remembers what he saw in detail. Judicial courts readily admit the testimony of an eyewitness as evidence during a trial. What did the apostle John in John 1:14 and the apostle Peter in 2 Peter 1:16 record that they saw and were eyewitnesses of?
   Christ's glory and majesty

But as it is written, Eye hath not seen, nor ear heard, neither have entered into the heart of man, the things which God hath prepared for them that love him. 1 Corinthians 2:9

Graphing   (Enhanced Practice; use after 9.1.)

Working down each column, plot each ordered pair, connecting the points with a straight line as you plot them. When you see the word *STOP*, lift your pencil to start a new section.

(−12, −11)	(−9, 2)	(0, 10)	(9, 0)	(1, −7)	(−5, −3)	(−3, 3)	(1, 1)
(−11, −9)	(−10, 2)	(−1, 11)	(9, −3)	(−3, −6)	(0, −1)	(−2, 2)	(1, 2)
(−9, −7)	(−10, 3)	(0, 10)	(7, −5)	(−5, −5)	(4, −3)	(−2, 1)	(2, 3)
(−8, −6)	(−8, 6)	(1, 11)	(4, −6)	STOP	(0, −1)	(−3, −1)	(3, 2)
(−9, −7)	(−7, 8)	(0, 10)	(5, −7)	(−5, −3)	(1, −4)	(−4, 0)	(4, 0)
(−11, −7)	(−3, 10)	(2, 9)	(7, −7)	(1, −4)	(0, −6)	(−5, 0)	(2, −1)
(−13, −6)	(−4, 11)	(4, 7)	(8, −9)	(4, −3)	STOP	(−4, 0)	(1, 1)
(−15, −4)	(−3, 10)	(6, 3)	(8, −11)	(2, −5)	(−7, −1)	(−3, 1)	(3, 1)
(−15, 0)	(−2, 11)	(5, 2)	STOP	(0, −6)	(−5, 0)	(−2, 1)	(4, 0)
(−13, 1)	(−3, 10)	(8, 1)	(4, −6)	(−2, −5)	(−5, 2)	STOP	STOP

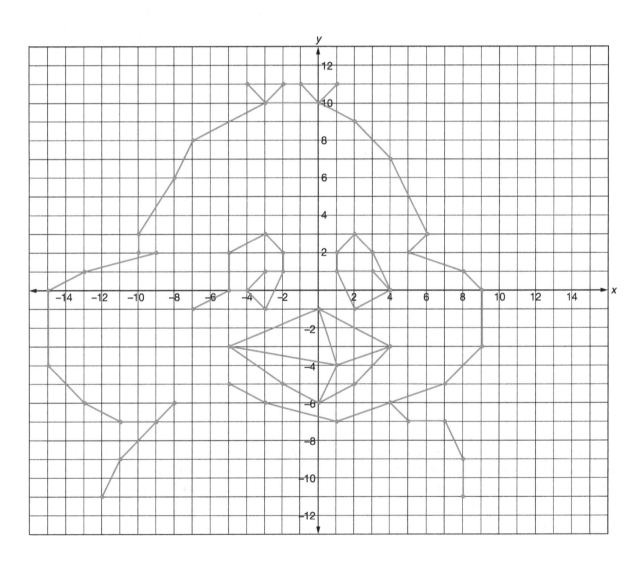

Poinsot Stars (Enrichment; use after 9.4.)

Early in the nineteenth century French mathematician Louis Poinsot developed a family of star-shaped designs. He started with points equally spaced around a circle and joined those points in a scheme that joined every adjacent point, every other point, then every third point, every fourth point, and so forth. A Poinsot star is said to be of order n if there are n vertices on the circle. The number of possible stars of order n is $\frac{n}{2}$ if n is an even number or $\frac{n-1}{2}$ if n is an odd number. Poinsot also classified the stars of order n as either *regular* or *compound*. Regular stars are formed when the joining scheme reaches all points before returning to the starting point. Compound stars require starting at more than one point in order to include all vertices. The table below summarizes this information for the first several orders.

Order	4	5	6	7	8	9	10	11
Number of Poinsot stars	2	2	3	3	4	4	5	5
Number of regular stars	1	2	1	3	2	3	2	5
Number of compound stars	1	0	2	0	2	1	3	0

Below are the four Poinsot stars of order 8. Can you identify the regular and compound ones?

Quite interesting designs result when all the stars of a given order are superimposed, meaning that all the cases are drawn on the same circle. The result is actually a regular polygon and all of its diagonals. Below are the superimposed stars for orders 7 and 11.

 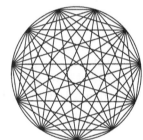

1. How many lines are in each figure of the superimposed Poinsot stars of orders 7 and 11? Count the number of lines from each point and then multiply by the number of points, but remember that you counted every line twice.

    order 7: 21 lines; order 11: 55 lines

2. Use the method of the last question to write a formula for the number of lines in all the superimposed stars of order n.

    number of lines = $\dfrac{n(n-1)}{2}$

3. Determine the number of possible Poinsot stars of order 13. Draw each possible Poinsot star of order 13, and then draw the superimposed stars. This last figure is a regular polygon with thirteen sides and all its diagonals. Use your own paper for some of the drawings if you need more space.

6 stars

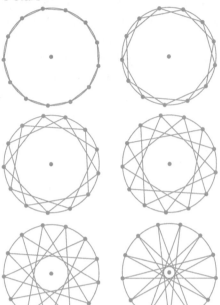

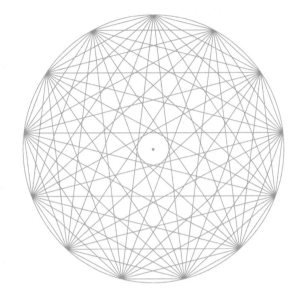

4. Poinsot gave the following formula for the number of regular stars in order n. If $p_1, p_2, \ldots, p_m$ are all the prime factors of n, and n is not prime, then $S(n) = \frac{n}{2} = \left(1 - \frac{1}{p_1}\right)\left(1 - \frac{1}{p_2}\right)\ldots\left(1 - \frac{1}{p_m}\right)$. Now find the number of regular stars for orders 9, 10, and 12. (Prime orders do not have compound stars.)

$S(9) = 3$, $S(10) = 2$, and $S(12) = 2$

5. The design below uses $n = 23$. The joining scheme connects each point to four other points, starting ten units away. So 1 joins to 11, 12, 13, and 14; 2 joins to 12, 13, 14, and 15; and so forth. Make your own design by using a value of n that is prime and greater than 23. It will help to divide the circle with a protractor and number the points.

Answers will vary.

Graphing Linear Functions   (Extra Practice; use after 9.6.)

Using a table, find at least three ordered pairs that satisfy the given function rules. Graph each linear equation.

1. $y = 3x + 2$

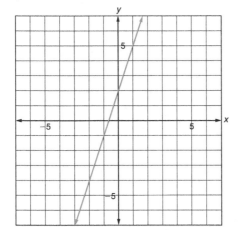

2. $y = -4x + 5$

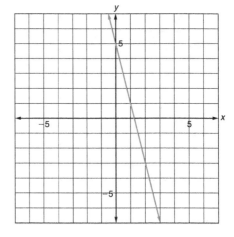

3. $y = \frac{3}{4}x$

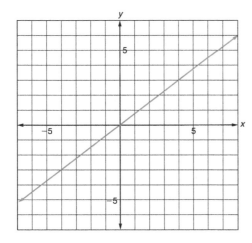

4. $y = 6(x - 1)$

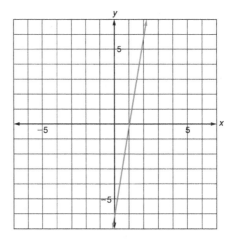

5. $5x + 2y = 20$

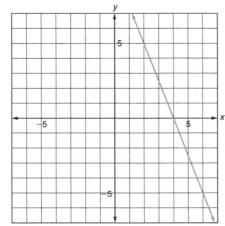

6. $y = -\frac{1}{3}x + 2$

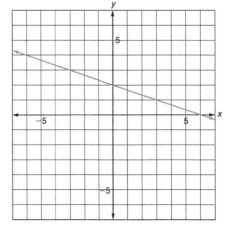

Use the *x*- and *y*-intercepts to graph the following lines.

7. $3x + 4y = 12$

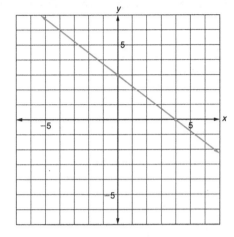

8. $y = -6x + 12$

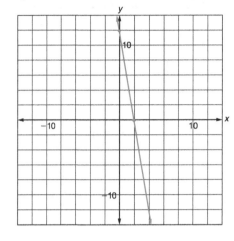

9. $y = \frac{2}{3}x - 6$

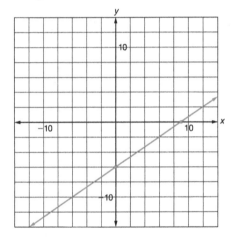

10. $y = 2 - \frac{1}{5}x$

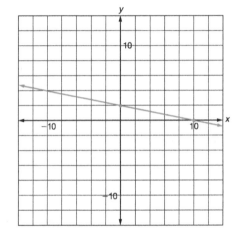

11. $7x - 2y = 14$

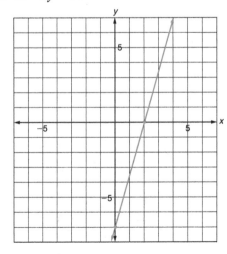

12. $y = 4x - 12$

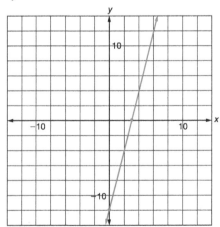

Chapter 9

Use the slope-intercept form to graph the following lines.

13. $y = \dfrac{5}{6}x - 2$

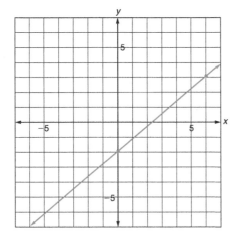

14. $6x - 7y = 28$

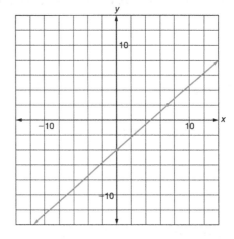

15. $y + 8 = -4x$

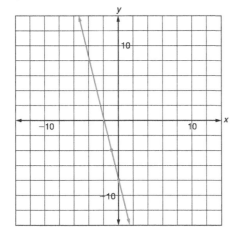

16. $4y = 16x$

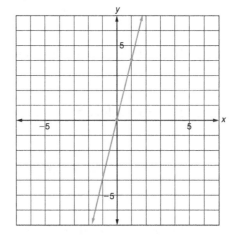

17. $y = -10 + \dfrac{2}{5}x$

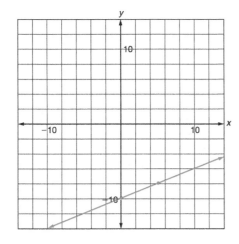

18. $15x - 25y = 50$

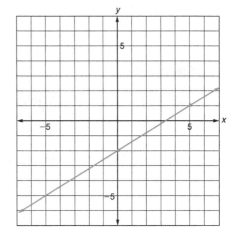

Direct Variation (Extra Practice; use after 9.7.)

Determine whether each equation represents a direct variation. Write *yes* or *no*.

_____yes_____ 1. $y = 8x$

_____no_____ 2. $w = 4(z - 2)$

_____yes_____ 3. $c = \pi d$

_____yes_____ 4. $p = \dfrac{\sqrt{2}q}{\pi}$

_____no_____ 5. $y = \pi x^{-1}$

_____no_____ 6. $PV = 480$

_____yes_____ 7. $2.5x + 3 = y + 3$

_____yes_____ 8. $\dfrac{P}{T} = \dfrac{\sqrt{5}}{2}$

Find the value of *k* for each direct variation.

_____7_____ 9. m varies directly with n and $m = 14$ when $n = 2$

_____$\frac{1}{6}$_____ 10. w varies directly with z and $w = -25$ when $z = -150$

_____$\frac{10}{\pi}$_____ 11. c varies directly with d and $c = 10\pi$ when $d = \pi^2$

_____$\frac{1}{10}$_____ 12. y varies directly with x and $y = 5$ when $x = 50$

_____10^{-3}_____ 13. h varies directly with g and $h = 10^{-8}$ when $g = 10^{-5}$

_____16_____ 14. b varies directly with c and $b = 128$ when $c = 2^3$

Find *y* if *y* varies directly with *x*.

_____8_____ 15. If $y = 2$ when $x = 16$, find y when $x = 64$.

_____$\frac{1}{10}$_____ 16. If $y = 10$ when $x = 10^4$, find y when $x = 100$.

_____4_____ 17. If $y = 16$ when $x = 4\sqrt{2}$, find y when $x = \sqrt{2}$.

_____π_____ 18. If $y = 2\sqrt{\pi}$ when $x = 2$, find y when $x = \sqrt{\pi}$.

Calculator Skill 9 (Use after 9.7.)

written for the TI-30Xa

Applications of Slope and Direct Variation

You have learned that $\frac{y}{x} = k$ and $y = kx$ both express a *direct variation* between the two variables x and y. They are also said to have the same ratio, which in some contexts is the slope of a line. The second form, $y = kx$, is easy to recognize as a linear equation defining a line with a slope of k and a y-intercept at $(0, 0)$, the origin. Remember that the slope of a line is the change in the y-coordinates divided by the change in the x-coordinates of two points on the line.

The number of real-life applications of direct variation is immense. A calculator is useful in solving these real-life problems because the numbers are often difficult to calculate without the use of available technology.

Example 1

Over a two-year period, the value of a certain make of car dropped from \$24,000 to \$18,200. If the depreciation rate remains constant over the next three years, what will the car's value be at that time?

Answer

$$\text{slope} = \frac{18{,}200 - 24{,}000}{2} = -2{,}900/\text{year (loss in value)}$$

$y = kx$ gives $y = 5(-2{,}900) = -14{,}500$ (loss over 5 yr.)

Therefore, the value at the end of five years is $24{,}000 - 14{,}500 = \$9{,}500$.

Example 2

The ratio of construction costs, M, to the buyer's cost, C, is a constant. If the construction costs were \$213,560 and the constant of variation is 0.698, what is the buyer's cost?

Answer

The ratio $\frac{M}{C} = 0.698$; therefore, $M = 0.698C$.

$0.698C = 213{,}560$

$$\frac{0.698C}{0.698} = \frac{213{,}560}{0.698}$$

$C = \$305{,}960$

Use your calculator to find the value of the unknown variable in each of the following direct variations. Use the π key on your calculator and round to the nearest thousandth.

_____ $r = 64.014$ _____ 1. $c = 2\pi r$; $c = 402.2123859$

_____ $a = 10.392$ _____ 2. $A = \frac{1}{2}ap$; $A = 374.1229744$ and $p = 72$

_____ $L = 164{,}870.783$ _____ 3. $L = 2\pi rH$; $r = 128$ and $H = 205$

_____ $m = 6.5$ kg _____ 4. $F = ma$; $F = 208$ kg $\cdot$ m/s^2 and $a = 32$ m/s^2

_____ $\mu = 0.380$ _____ 5. $\mu = \dfrac{f}{N}$; $N = 180.5$ and $f = 68.5$

_____ $A = 108.108$ _____ 6. $P = \dfrac{F}{A}$; $P = 185$ and $F = 2 \times 10^4$

_____ $W_o = 226{,}625$ BTU _____ 7. $e = \dfrac{W_o}{W_I}$; $e = 92.5\%$ and $W_I = 2.45 \times 10^5$ BTU

_____ $\lambda = 6 \times 10^{-7}$ m/cycle _____ 8. $\lambda = \dfrac{c}{f}$; $c = 3 \times 10^8$ m/sec. and $f = 5 \times 10^{14}$ cycles/sec.

9. The circumference and diameter of a circle form a direct variation. The constant of variation is π. What is the circumference of a circle with a diameter of 18 m?
   $c = 56.549$ m

10. A tunnel through a mountain a mile wide enters at one end at an elevation of 5,865 ft. above sea level and exits at the other end at an elevation of 6,025 ft. above sea level. Find the average slope of this tunnel; then express this slope as a percent.
    $m = 0.030$; 3.0%

11. A highway takes traffic from an elevation of 4,560 ft. above sea level on a meandering path up a mountain and across the Continental Divide. If the average slope is 4% and the horizontal length of the road is 12.5 mi. from the base to the Continental Divide, at what elevation is the Continental Divide on this highway?
    elevation = 7,200 ft.

12. The amount of consumer credit in the United States increased from $838.6 billion in 1993 to $1,235.8 billion in 1997. What was the average increase per year?
    average increase = $99.3 billion/yr.

13. Suppose in a given metropolitan area the market price of a home in 1989 was $135,500 and in 1999 the price had increased to $175,500. What is the average yearly increase? Assuming the same rate of increase, what would you expect the price to be in 2012?
    average increase = $4,000/yr.; $227,500 in 2012

Problem Solving—Function Applications (Use after 9.7.)

1. A person's weight on the moon is directly proportional to his weight on the earth. Fill in the missing entries in the following table and write an equation relating weight in pounds on the moon (m) to weight in pounds on the earth (e).

m	15	16.7	25	33.3
e	90	100	150	200

    $m = \frac{1}{6}e$

2. A workout facility offers a standard membership for a $200 entry fee and $40 per month or a premium membership for a $300 entry fee and $30 per month. After how many months will the premium membership be less expensive?

    after 10 months

3. Katie's cat, Odyssey, has three kittens with identical weights. If Odyssey weighs 4 kg and the whole cat family weights 5.5 kg, how much does each kitten weigh?

    0.5 kg

4. A trip from Superior, Montana, to the state line near Mullan, Idaho, on I-90 covers 47 mi. and goes from an elevation of 2,760 ft. to 4,700 ft. What is the average percent grade?

    0.8%

5. DriveAway car rentals charges $45 per day plus $0.12 per mile after the first 150 mi. StarDrive car rentals charges $35 per day plus $0.14 per mile after the first 100 mi. For a three-day rental, after how many miles will DriveAway be less expensive?

    1,300 mi.

6. Gliders get lift from their wings by their descent speed since they have no engine. Many gliders have a 60 : 1 glide ratio (slope). This means that they can travel 60 mi. for each 1 mi. (5,280 ft.) up. How many feet above a desired landing spot is a glider released if it lands 42 mi. from the release spot? At what altitude will the glider start if it lands on a strip at an elevation of 3,200 ft.?

    3,696 ft.; 6,896 ft.

7. Retailers often see a linear relationship between the price they charge for an item and the number of sales per week or per day. The following table gives the price per dozen roses and the resulting sales in dozens per week. It is clear that increasing prices decreases sales, so the slope of the linear function is negative.

Price/dozen	$15	$18	$21	$24
Sales in dozens	45	40	35	30

    a. Using ordered pairs (price, sales), find the slope of the function.

    $m = -\frac{5}{3}$

    b. The equation that relates the price (p) and the sales (s) is $s = -\frac{5}{3}p + 70$.

    Find the sales when the price is $30 per dozen, and find the price at which sales would drop to zero.

    20 dozen; $42

Chapter 9 Review

Write T for true or F for false. If the statement is false, correct it.

_____T_____ 1. A quadrant is a region of the coordinate plane determined by its axes.

_____F_____ 2. A function is defined as any set of ordered pairs.
change "function" to "relation"

_____T_____ 3. Some functions can be described by an equation.

_____F_____ 4. The range of a function is the set of x-coordinates.
change "range" to "domain" or "x-coordinates" to "y-coordinates"

_____F_____ 5. The slope of a function is the ratio comparing the run to the rise.
change the phrase "run to the rise" to "rise to the run"

Fill in the blank.

_____coordinate plane_____ 6. A(n) ___ is determined by two intersecting number lines.

_____x-axis_____ 7. The ___ is the horizontal number line.

_____function_____ 8. A relation in which no two x-coordinates are the same is called a(n) ___.

_____y-intercept_____ 9. The ___ is the location at which a line intersects the y-axis.

Graph each point in the same coordinate plane.

10. $(-2, -4)$

11. $(6, 5)$

12. $(0, -5)$

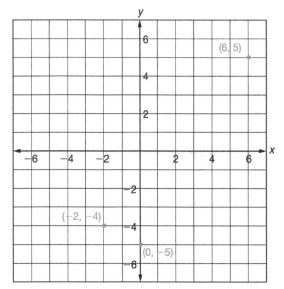

Give the domain and range of each relation and determine whether it is a function.

13. {(1, 2), (3, 4), (–1, –2), (–3, –4)}
$D = \{-3, -1, 1, 3\}; R = \{-4, -2, 2, 4\}$; yes

14. {(2, 2), (2, 3), (2, 4), (2, 5), (2, 6)}
$D = \{2\}; R = \{2, 3, 4, 5, 6\}$; no

If $f(x) = 2x + 5$, find the following.

_____5_____ 15. $f(0)$ _____3_____ 16. $f(-1)$ _____11_____ 17. $f(3)$

Find the range of the functions with the given domains.

18. $f(x) = 4x - 5; D = \{-2, -1, 0, 2, 3\}$
$R = \{-13, -9, -5, 3, 7\}$

19. $f(x) = -2x + 8; D = \{-3, 0, 2, 6\}$
$R = \{-4, 4, 8, 14\}$

Determine which of the given ordered pairs are solutions to the linear equation and list them.

_____(1, 1)_____ 20. $y = -4x + 5$; (1, 1) and (1, 9)

___(3, –1) and (–6, –4)___ 21. $y = \frac{1}{3}x - 2$; (3, –1) and (–6, –4)

For each equation, make a table of ordered pair solutions for the given x values.

22. $y = 3x - 2$ for $x = -2, -1, 0, 1, 2$

x	y
–2	–8
–1	–5
0	–2
1	1
2	4

23. $y = -6x + 8$ for $x = -3, -1, 0, 3, 4$

x	y
–3	26
–1	14
0	8
3	–10
4	–16

Find the slope of the line through the two given points.

_____$-\frac{2}{3}$_____ 24. $C(-2, 5), D(4, 1)$

_____–2_____ 25. $C(6, 2), D(4, 6)$

Find the slope and *y*-intercept of the following lines.

_____*m* = 2; (0, −5)_____ 26. $y = 2x - 5$

_____*m* = −3; (0, 4)_____ 27. $-3x + 4 = y$

Determine whether each table of values represents a direct variation. If it does, find the constant of variation.

28. ___yes; *k* = 2___

x	y
3	6
4	8
5	10

29. ___no___

x	y
1	18
2	9
3	6

30. ___no___

x	y
3	−12
0	0
−1	4

Graph the following linear equations on the same coordinate plane.

31. $2x + 3 = y$

32. $y = -2x - 1$

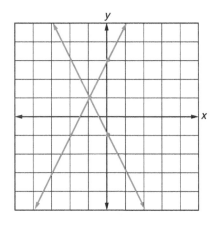

Graph the solution to the following inequality.

33. $y > 5x + 4$

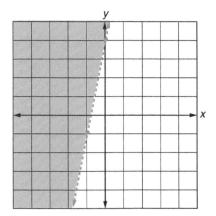

Cumulative Review 9

_____c_____ 1. Evaluate $4(x - y) + 8z$ when $x = -3$, $y = 6$, and $z = 2$.
   a. 4
   b. 28
   c. −20
   d. −12
   e. none of these

_____b_____ 2. Evaluate $a^2 + b^3$ when $a = -1$ and $b = 3$.
   a. −26
   b. 28
   c. 10
   d. 26
   e. none of these

_____e_____ 3. The W&J Cowboy Shop has jeans on sale for $37.70, which represents a 35% discount. What was the original price of the jeans?
   a. $93
   b. $50
   c. $40
   d. $30
   e. none of these

_____a_____ 4. The distance between two major cities on a map is 4.5 cm. If the scale is 1 cm : 25 mi., how far is it between the cities?
   a. 112.5 mi.
   b. 100 mi.
   c. 125 mi.
   d. 555 mi.
   e. none of these

_____c_____ 5. If 3,982 of the 5,025 seats in the auditorium are filled, what percent of the seats are empty?
   a. 26%
   b. 79%
   c. 21%
   d. 44%
   e. none of these

_____c_____ 6. Mr. Bazzle usually leaves at least an 18% tip for a waitress. If the total meal price for his family is $64, what is the least amount (to the nearest dollar) that he should leave as a tip?
   a. $11
   b. $10
   c. $12
   d. $13
   e. none of these

_____d_____ 7. Subtract $132_5 - 23_5$.
   a. 111_5
   b. 109_5
   c. 102_5
   d. 104_5
   e. none of these

_____a_____ 8. Solve $\frac{(x + 2)}{8} = \frac{5}{9}$.
   a. $\frac{22}{9}$
   b. $\frac{58}{9}$
   c. $\frac{38}{9}$
   d. $\frac{9}{22}$
   e. none of these

_____b_____ 9. Convert $\frac{7}{9}$ to a decimal.

     a. $1.\overline{285714}$ d. 0.77

     b. $0.\overline{7}$ e. none of these

     c. 0.7

_____c_____ 10. Add $\frac{4}{27} + 8$.

     a. $\frac{12}{35}$ d. $8\frac{1}{9}$

     b. $\frac{12}{27}$ e. none of these

     c. $\frac{220}{27}$

_____a_____ 11. Solve $-5x + 6 = -39$.

     a. 9   d. $-\frac{33}{5}$

     b. -9 e. none of these

     c. $\frac{33}{5}$

_____c_____ 12. Solve $3(4y - 7) - 16 = -85$.

     a. $-\frac{15}{2}$ d. $\frac{61}{6}$

     b. $-\frac{61}{6}$ e. none of these

     c. -4

_____b_____ 13. Solve $8w - 17 = 2(w + 4)$.

     a. $-\frac{3}{2}$ d. $\frac{7}{2}$

     b. $\frac{25}{6}$ e. none of these

     c. $\frac{5}{2}$

_____e_____ 14. Find the percent change if the price of a computer goes from $2,245 to $1,850.

     a. 21% decrease   d. 18% increase

     b. 82% decrease   e. none of these

     c. 21% increase

_____d_____ 15. A jet flying against the wind can make a 930 km flight in 1.5 hr. If the average wind speed is 20 km/hr., what is the jet's air speed?

     a. 950 km/hr.   d. 640 km/hr.

     b. 1,350 km/hr.   e. none of these

     c. 600 km/hr.

10 Statistics and Probability

Creation Wonders—The Human Ear   (Bible Activity; use after 10.1.)

The human ear functions both as the receiver of sound and as the balance center of the body. God created us with two ears, which allows us to locate sounds. Sound moves in waves of energy through the air and other materials, and the ear changes these waves into nerve impulses that are transmitted to the brain. The brain does the actual hearing as it processes the information from the nerves.

There are three parts of the ear—the outer ear, the middle ear, and the inner ear. The outer ear channels the sound waves to the eardrum, which vibrates with the sound waves. The eardrum is connected to three bones in the middle ear, which move with the eardrum, amplifying the vibrations. These vibrations cause waves in the liquid filling the inner ear. The inner ear contains microscopic hair cells that protrude into the fluid. The waves bend the hair cells, causing nerve impulses that the brain interprets as sound. All of this takes places at speeds so fast that it seems as though everything occurs instantaneously.

Hearing loss is a major problem among young people today. About 12.5% of American young people ages 6–19 have permanent damage to the hair cells in the inner ear due to excessively loud noise. The intensity of sound is measured in decibels (dB). The decibel, named after Alexander Graham Bell, is a ratio that compares the sound intensity to a known level. Sounds at a high intensity ($\geq$ 85 dB), especially those of long duration, can cause damage to the inner ear.

The decibel scale is not a linear scale as, for instance, the scales we use in measuring length: While 20 ft. is twice as long as 10 ft., 20 dB is ten times more intense than 10 dB. Every increase of 10 dB is caused by sound that is actually ten (10^1) times more intense. So 30 dB is ten times as intense as 20 dB, 40 dB is one hundred times as intense as 20 dB, and so on. When you are comparing two sounds, the intensity is changed by a factor of 10^x, where x is the difference between the two decibel levels divided by 10. For instance, 50 dB is 10,000 times more intense than 10 dB because $(50 - 10) \div 10 = 4$, the exponent in 10^4.

Mark 7:32–37 records the miracle of Jesus' healing a deaf man. The passage concludes with the effect of this miracle on the observers: "And [they] were beyond measure astonished, saying, He hath done all things well: he maketh both the deaf to hear, and the dumb to speak."

1. In cultures where few people can read or where access to written material is limited, God's gift of hearing is essential. What do the prophets admonish the people to do in Isaiah 66:5 and Jeremiah 2:4?
   hear the Word of the Lord

2. What precious gift is obtained by hearing, according to Romans 10:17?
   faith

3. The quiet surroundings of a public library have a sound intensity level of approximately 40 dB. If the sound of a jet taking off is 140 dB, how many times as intense is the sound of a jet taking off than the sound in a quiet library? Could the sound of a jet taking off damage the sense of hearing?
   10^{10} or 10 billion; yes

4. If amplified music ranges in intensity from 110 to 130 dB, how many times as intense is it than the loudest sounds that have little risk of causing hearing loss (80 dB)?
   1,000–100,000 times

> *And Moses called all Israel, and said unto them, Hear, O Israel, the statutes and judgments which I speak in your ears this day, that ye may learn them, and keep, and do them.* Deuteronomy 5:1

Statistical Sampling (Enrichment; use after 10.4.)
See the teacher notes at the end of this activity.

Purpose
Take samples from a bag of colored candies in order to predict population parameters. For the purposes of this experiment, the whole bag of candies is the population. From the data collected using the sample, you will construct a frequency distribution table and a bar graph. These statistical displays will give you an understanding of the distribution of colors within the entire bag.

Materials
a large bag of colored candies (Any type of small candy that comes in bags containing several different colors will work for this activity.)

a large bowl

a small measuring cup or a large serving spoon (should hold about 16 to 25 candies)

extra paper

colored pencils

Predictions
List the colors found in the bag of candies. Which color do you think occurs most often? Which color do you think occurs least often?

Sampling
Pour the bag of candies into the bowl and mix thoroughly. Then randomly scoop up a sample and pour it out. Write down how many candies of each color are in the sample, as well as how many total candies are in the sample. Replace the candies and remix the entire amount. Take at least six samples per group or individual. (Make sure your hands and equipment are clean—at the end of the experiment you may want to eat your candies.)

Frequency Distribution
Make a frequency distribution table of the data. List the colors in the data column and your totals for each color in the frequency column. Instead of a product column, make a percent distribution column. You can find the percent distribution by dividing the number of a single color by the total number of candies sampled. These sample parameters are predictive of the distribution of colors within the entire bag of candies.

Bar Graph
Make a bar graph of the data. You will need as many bars as there are colors; label the bars along the horizontal axis. Remember that the height of each bar measures the frequency of that color. If you use colored pencils to make the bars the appropriate colors, this graph will make an excellent visual representation of the color distribution.

Conclusions
1. Which color would you expect to find most often in the entire bag of candies?

2. Which color would you expect to find least often in the entire bag of candies?

3. If your sample consisted of about one-seventh of the population, how many of each color of candies would you expect to find in the entire bag?

This experiment gives each student an opportunity to generate his own statistics and graphs based on his samples. If an individual student is doing the experiment, he will need to take several samples. If students are working in groups of three or four, each individual will take a sample or two and then combine his results with those of the rest of the people in that group.

Problem Solving—Using Graphs (Use after 10.5.)

Note: Be sure to accept reasonable approximations of the exact answers given.

For each of the following problems, draw a line through the points on the given graph to estimate the solution.

1. A furniture salesman's earnings from his weekly sales are graphed below.

   a. How much would he earn in a week in which he makes no sales?
      $400

   b. Estimate his income if he sells $12,000 worth of furniture in a given week.
      $1,360

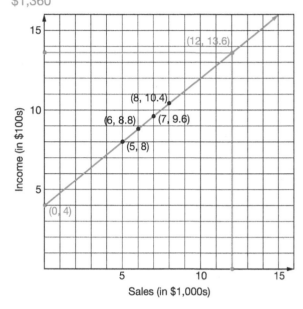

2. The following graph relates the water pressure experienced by a scuba diver to the depth that he descends below the surface of the water.

   a. Find how deep a diver can go and not exceed 30 psi of water pressure.
      70 ft.

   b. Divers must have special certification to go below 60 ft. and 120 ft. What are the water pressures at these two depths?
      ≈ 26 psi; ≈ 51 psi

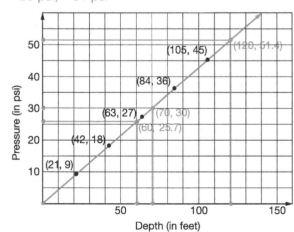

3. A new car cost $24,000, and its value two years later was $18,200. Assume a constant depreciation rate for the first six years.

 a. What will the car's value be after five years?

 $9,500

 b. When will its value be $15,000?

 after 3.1 yr.

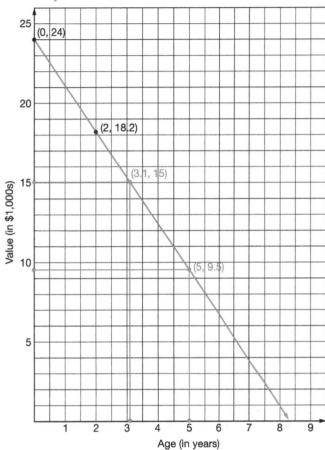

4. The population of a certain Midwestern city was 52,500 in 2000 and 62,500 in 2004.

 a. In what year would the population reach 75,000?

 2009

 b. If the growth remains about the same, what would the population be in 2020?

 102,500

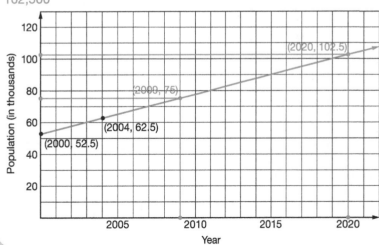

Calculator Skill 10 (Use after 10.7.)

written for the TI-30Xa

Permutations

Remember that the number of possible permutations of n objects when all of them are used is $_nP_n = n!$. When only r at a time are taken and arranged, the number of permutations is $_nP_r = \dfrac{n!}{(n-r)!}$. The calculator has a permutation function, found above the 9 key.

Example 1

Calculate $_8P_8$.

Answer

Keystrokes: 8 [nPr] ([2nd] 9) 8 [=]
Result: 40,320

Combinations

Remember that the number of possible combinations of n objects taken r at a time is $_nC_r = \dfrac{n!}{(n-r)!r!}$. Recall that dividing by $r!$ eliminates the different arrangements of the same r objects. The calculator's combination function is found above the 8 key.

Example 2

Calculate $_8C_3$.

Answer

Keystrokes: 8 [nCr] ([2nd] 8) 3 [=]
Result: 56

Use your calculator to find the following permutations and combinations.

1,814,400	1. $_{10}P_8$		45	2. $_{10}C_8$
1	3. $_{15}P_0$		792	4. $_{12}C_5$
362,880	5. $_9P_9$		1	6. $_{15}C_0$
3,268,760	7. $_{25}C_{15}$		1	8. $_{50}C_{50}$

Use your calculator to find the number of permutations or combinations for each of the following word problems.

9. How many committees of three are possible in a group of ten people?

   120

10. How many different combination padlocks can be made when each entrance code uses three different numbers from the thirty-nine possible on the lock?

    54,834

11. Reasoning from your answer to exercise 10, do you think a lock manufacturer makes more than one lock with the same combination? Why or why not?

    Yes; if the locks are produced over several years, more than 54,000 will be produced.

12. A bank is making group photos of its twenty executives. If there are five people in each picture, how many different ways can these photos be made if changing the order in which the executives line up is considered a different picture? Suppose it is not considered a different picture?

    1,860,480; 15,504

13. At the Burger Stand Ken puts five different condiments (such as tomato, lettuce, etc.) on each burger. If there are eight of these extras to choose from, how many different ways can he build a burger?

    56

14. At the Smoky Mountains Cafeteria a large meal consists of choosing two salads, three vegetables, one meat, one drink, and two breads. How many different meals can a customer choose if the serving counter has six salads, eight vegetables, five meats, six drinks, and four breads?

    151,200

15. The local yogurt store sells plain yogurt with any combination of six toppings. If customers can choose zero, one, two, or all the way up to six toppings, how many possible yogurt desserts can be ordered?

    64

Combinations (Enhanced Practice; use after 10.7.)

Remember that a *combination* is a selection or set in which the order does not matter. When a problem involves several steps, multiply the combinations for each selection. This is an application of the Fundamental Principle of Counting. However, if the problem involves making one selection *or* another, add the number of ways the individual components can be selected.

Example

How many different committees of three can be selected from five women and four men if the committee must have at least one man and at least one woman?

Answer

The selection of the committee can be done two different ways to meet the criteria of the problem. You can pick one man and two women or one woman and two men.

The number of ways one man and two women can be selected is a product of the number of ways one man can be selected from four men ($_4C_1$) and the number of ways two women can be selected from five women ($_5C_2$). This is an application of the Fundamental Principle of Counting.

The other possibility is selecting one woman and two men. The number of ways two men can be selected from four men is $_4C_2$, and the number of ways one woman can be selected from five women is $_5C_1$.

Since the solution could be one man and two women or two men and one woman, the products are added to find the total number of ways the committee can be formed.

$$_4C_1 \cdot {_5C_2} + {_4C_2} \cdot {_5C_1} = 4 \cdot 10 + 6 \cdot 5 = 40 + 30 = 70$$

Use the formula for combinations to solve the following exercises.

1. The classic question about selecting meals at a cafeteria-style restaurant involves combinations because the order of the selection is not important. You are typically making selections in succession, so the individual combination counts are multiplied. How many ways can you select one each from a choice of four salads, three entrees, four vegetables, three breads, five drinks, and six desserts?
   4,320

2. How many possible outfits can you select from twelve shirts, six pairs of pants, and three pairs of shoes?
   216

3. How many different groups of five players can a basketball coach use to start a game if he has ten players on his roster?
   252

4. How many different twelve-person juries can be formed from a jury pool of 45 people?
   2.876×10^{10}

5. How many committees of four can be selected from a group of six Republicans and five Democrats if at least one member of each party must be on the committee?
310

6. If a soccer league has eight teams, each of which plays two games with each of the other teams, how many games will be played?
56

7. You can choose from zero to four toppings on your ice cream sundae. How many different sundaes could you order?
16

8. Suppose you are buying a dozen doughnuts from a shop that has eighteen different kinds of doughnuts. How many different ways can you get your dozen doughnuts if you select only one of each kind?
18,564

Identify each of the following as a permutation (_P_) or a combination (_C_). Do not solve.

_____ P _____ 9. From the twelve letters in the Hawaiian alphabet, how many five-letter "words" can you make?

_____ C _____ 10. The sheriff has eight deputies that he needs to divide into two posses to chase a bank robber. If each posse must have at least two deputies, how many different pairs of posses can he form?

_____ P _____ 11. How many three-digit numbers can be made from the numbers {1, 2, 3, 4, 5, 6}?

_____ C _____ 12. How many matching pairs can be selected in the dark from a drawer of socks containing four white, eight black, and four navy socks?

_____ P _____ 13. How many different license plates could be made using either one or two letters followed by any grouping of one to five numbers?

_____ C _____ 14. A retailer buys from five local companies and twelve online companies. How many ways can he place an order for four specialty items if two come from each source?

_____ P _____ 15. How many Social Security numbers are possible if the numbers have the form 432-40-2323?

Chapter 10 Review

Write T for true or F for false. If the statement is false, correct it or give an example showing why it is false.

___T___ 1. Statistics studies the collection, organization, and analysis of numerical information.

___F___ 2. *Average* is another word for *median*.
  change "median" to "mean"

___F___ 3. There can be only one mode in a data set.
  In the set {2, 3, 2, 3, 5}, 2 and 3 are modes; in the set {1, 2, 3, 4}, there is no mode.

___T___ 4. Probability is the chance that something will happen.

___T___ 5. The frequency distribution table is used to organize information.

6. The Smiths' grocery bills in May were $85.58, $95.00, $79.70, $92.58, and $103.26. Find the mean, median, and mode. Round to the nearest cent if necessary.
  mean: $91.22; median: $92.58; mode: none

7. Find the mean, median, mode, lower quartile, upper quartile, and range of the following set of data: {37, 42, 62, 38, 51, 54, 48, 54, 49, 54}.
  mean: 48.9; median: 50; mode: 54; lower quartile: 42; upper quartile: 54; range: 25

8. Construct a box-and-whisker diagram for the data in exercise 7.

37   42   50 54   62

Identify the following samples as random, systematic, convenience, or cluster.

___systematic___ 9. every tenth person in the phone book

___convenience___ 10. each person who enters the mall on May 14

___random___ 11. All the names of the students in the school are written on slips of paper and put in a box. Fifteen names are drawn from the box by a first-grader.

12. Make a stem-and-leaf diagram of the ages of the first forty-four presidents of the United States at the time of their inagurations: {57, 61, 57, 57, 58, 57, 61, 54, 68, 51, 49, 64, 50, 48, 65, 52, 56, 46, 54, 49, 50, 47, 55, 55, 54, 42, 51, 56, 55, 51, 54, 51, 60, 62, 43, 55, 56, 61, 52, 69, 64, 46, 54, 47}.

```
4 | 2  3  6  6  7  7  8  9  9
5 | 0  0  1  1  1  1  2  2  4  4  4  4  4  5  5  5  5  6  6  6  7  7  7  7  8
6 | 0  1  1  1  2  4  4  5  8  9
```

13. Construct a scatterplot comparing the weight of people on the earth and on the moon. Determine whether there is a positive or negative correlation.

Weight on the Earth	Weight on the Moon
115	19
150	24.9
200	33.2
182	30.2
95	15.7
107	17.7
138	22.9
174	28.8
100	16.6
145	24

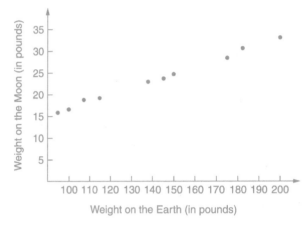

positive

14. The high-school band is made up of nine freshmen, fifteen sophomores, twenty-four juniors, and sixteen seniors. Make a bar graph to represent this data.

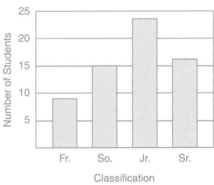

15. In four successive years a high-school football team had the following numbers of players: 25, 30, 40, and 34. Make a line graph to represent this data.

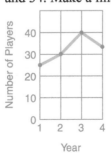

16. Use the following set of quiz scores to make a frequency distribution table. Find the mean, median, mode, and range: {3, 10, 8, 9, 7, 8, 6, 9, 10, 9, 7, 8, 9, 8, 7}.

mean: 7.9; median: 8; mode: 8 and 9; range: 7

Frequency Distribution Table			
Data (D)	Tally	Frequency (f)	Product (Df)
3			1	3
6			1	6
7					3	21
8						4	32
9						4	36
10				2	20
Total		15	118

17. Construct a histogram for the data in the following table.

Temperature (°F)	Frequency (days)
61–70	2
71–80	14
81–90	12
91–100	3

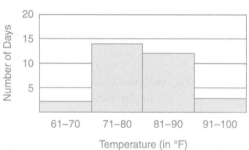

18. Make a pie chart for the following data concerning the production of tart cherries in the United States.

State	Production (millions of pounds)
Colorado	2.4
Michigan	80
New York	23
Oregon	7
Pennsylvania	6.5
Utah	14.5
Wisconsin	6.5

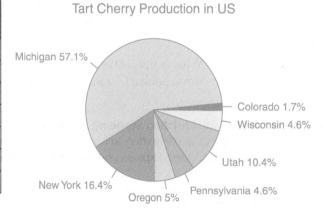

Tart Cherry Production in US

Evaluate.

_____720_____ 19. $6!$

_____24_____ 20. $_4P_4$

_____840_____ 21. $_7P_4$

_____126_____ 22. $_9C_4$

_____120_____ 23. How many ways can five different bicycles be arranged in a line?

_____18_____ 24. Find the total number of possible choices of a sandwich and dessert from six sandwiches and three desserts.

_____24_____ 25. Find the total number of different three-digit numbers possible if the first digit is 1, 3, or 5; the second is 0 or 5; and the third is 2, 4, 6, or 8.

_____1,716_____ 26. How many ways can a coach combine thirteen available players on a six-player volleyball team?

Four blue balls, eight white balls, and two green balls are placed in a jar. Find each of the following probabilities. Express your answer as both a fraction and a decimal rounded to the nearest hundredth.

_____$\frac{1}{7} \approx 0.14$_____ 27. What is the probability that a green ball will be drawn?

_____$\frac{3}{7} \approx 0.43$_____ 28. What is the probability that a blue or a green ball will be drawn?

_____$\frac{16}{49} \approx 0.33$_____ 29. What is the probability of drawing two white balls if the first ball is put back in the jar before the second ball is drawn?

_____$\frac{4}{91} \approx 0.04$_____ 30. What is the probability of drawing a blue ball followed by a green ball if the first ball is not put back in the jar before the second ball is drawn?

Of the 180 boys in Faith Christian Academy, 38 participate in the sports program and 46 participate in the music program, with 12 participating in both. A single student in the school is chosen at random. Find each of the following probabilities. Express your answer as both a fraction and a decimal rounded to the nearest hundredth.

_____$\frac{2}{5} = 0.4$_____ 31. P(a boy in sports or in the music program)

_____$\frac{1}{15} \approx 0.07$_____ 32. P(a boy in sports and in the music program)

_____$\frac{6}{23} \approx 0.26$_____ 33. P(a boy in sports, given that he is in the music program)

Cumulative Review 10

<u> c </u> 1. Add $7 + (-16) + 9 + (-8)$.

     a. 40   d. −26

     b. 8   e. none of these

     c. −8

<u> b </u> 2. Write 5,300,000,000 in scientific notation.

     a. 53×10^8 d. 530×10^7

     b. 5.3×10^9 e. none of these

     c. 5.3×10^8

<u> b </u> 3. Identify the property used: $(7x - 28) = 7(x - 4)$.

     a. Associative   d. Closure

     b. Distributive   e. none of these

     c. Commutative

<u> d </u> 4. Estimate $602(4,850 + 8,067)$ by rounding.

     a. 8,000,000   d. 7,800,000

     b. 9,100,000   e. none of these

     c. 7,200,000

<u> a </u> 5. Solve $4x - 19 = x + 17$.

     a. 12   d. 108

     b. $\frac{-1}{2}$ e. none of these

     c. $\frac{-2}{3}$

<u> e </u> 6. Solve $-6y + 8 \leq -16$.

     a. $y \leq -4$ d. $y = 4$

     b. $y \geq -4$ e. none of these

     c. $y \leq 4$

<u> c </u> 7. Which of the following numbers is prime?

     a. 91   d. 221

     b. 99   e. none of these

     c. 109

<u> c </u> 8. Find the GCF of 140 and 294.

     a. 196   d. 98

     b. 15   e. none of these

     c. 14

_____c_____ 9. Which of the following numbers is the greatest?

a. $\frac{3}{8}$

b. $\frac{7}{18}$

c. $\frac{5}{11}$

d. $\frac{4}{9}$

e. none of these

_____a_____ 10. Jake needs at least 92 points on the next English test to bring his class average up to an A. If there are 25 four-point multiple-choice questions on the test, how many of them does he need to get correct to make an A?

a. 23 or more

b. more than 23

c. less than 23

d. 22 or more

e. none of these

_____d_____ 11. Solve $\frac{1}{5}\left(x + \frac{2}{3}\right) = \frac{2}{5}$.

a. $-\frac{1}{4}$

b. $\frac{8}{3}$

c. 0

d. $\frac{4}{3}$

e. none of these

_____e_____ 12. Evaluate $\frac{a - 2b}{b^2}$ when $a = 0.2$ and $b = -3.5$.

a. −0.587755

b. −0.555102

c. 0.555102

d. −2.05714

e. none of these

_____c_____ 13. What percent of 1,982 is 1,500 (to the nearest percent)?

a. 75%

b. 132%

c. 76%

d. 24%

e. none of these

_____b_____ 14. What is a relation?

a. a set of even numbers

b. any set of ordered pairs

c. a set of ordered pairs in which the x value is used more than once

d. a set of numbers that are multiples of 3

e. none of these

_____a_____ 15. If $f(x) = 8x + 9$, what is $f(6)$?

a. 57

b. 39

c. 62

d. −39

e. none of these

11 Radicals

Creation Wonders—The Human Heart (Bible Activity; use after 11.1.)

Our Creator's design of the human heart stands as a circulatory masterpiece both in function and in longevity. As we sleep the heart can "rest" by pumping more slowly, but during strenuous exercise it must adjust to pump five or six times more blood to meet the respiratory demands of the body. The average heart beats 36.8 million times a year and 2.58 billion times over a seventy-year life span. Man-made pumping machinery could never last seventy or eighty years without replacement, yet the little 320 g pump beating in the human chest never stops as it pumps 180.3 million L of blood over a seventy-year life span.

Of course, we all know that if our heart stopped beating, we would die. Since all the cells in our bodies need blood to supply them with food and oxygen, our heart sends fresh oxygenated blood to the cells through the arteries and brings back oxygen-depleted blood through the veins. Branching like the twigs of a large oak tree, the arteries get smaller and smaller down to the capillary level. The capillaries come together to form veins, which get larger and larger on their way back to the heart. The 1.2 billion capillaries supplying all the cells represent 1,200,000 m of "tubing" that is only about 0.008 mm in diameter. This wonderful circulatory system connects all the organs. As you will see in a later chapter, the blood has a number of other functions that are essential to life, all of which depend on that wonderful little pump—the heart.

1. The Scriptures contain hundreds of references to the heart, but be careful: they refer to ideas such as the will, courage, the soul, or the seat of the emotions. In Exodus 7:13–14 what does the reference to Pharaoh's heart actually mean?

   He stubbornly refused to listen to God and let Israel go.

2. Since the diameter of the earth at the equator is about 12,756 km, how many adults would it take for their combined capillaries to reach around the earth?

   34

3. Knowing the number of heartbeats in a seventy-year life span and the total number of liters of blood pumped, how much blood is pumped at each beat (to the nearest milliliter)?

   70 mL/beat

4. If the total blood volume of an adult is about 5 L, how many heartbeats does it take for the blood to make one complete cycle?

   71 beats (about 1 min.)

> *My son, attend to my words; incline thine ear unto my sayings. Let them not depart from thine eyes; keep them in the midst of thine heart. For they are life unto those that find them, and health to all their flesh. Keep thy heart with all diligence; for out of it are the issues of life.* Proverbs 4:20–23

Problem Solving—Working Backwards (Use after 11.1.)

Devise a plan for each problem based on the strategy of working backwards; then carry out the plan and check your answer.

1. A furniture store had a series of "going out of business" sales (each discount was on top of the previous sale). First was 30% off, next half price, then 60% off, and finally 70% off. If a china cabinet cost a buyer $100 at the final sale, what was its original price?

   $2,380.95

2. The late J. D. Wise left half of his wealth to his alma mater. Three-fourths of what remained went to his three children in equal amounts. Of the remaining amount, half went to the YMCA and the remaining $10 million went to various mission enterprises. What was the size of this estate, and how much did each beneficiary receive?

   total: $160 million; alma mater: $80 million, each child: $20 million, YMCA: $10 million, and missions: $10 million

3. In the days of yore a young man went to pick apples in the king's orchard. The king, of course, wanted his share; so he had seven gates at which his officials collected taxes. If the tax collector at each of the seven gates required half of the young man's apples, how many baskets did he start out with if he had only one left at the end?

   128 baskets

4. A conscientious commuter always drives the speed limit when she makes the 25 mi. trip to work. She drives at 35 mi./hr. for 6 min., drives twice as long at 55 mi./hr. as she does at 45 mi./hr., and drives the final leg of her trip at 70 mi./hr. for 12 min. How long does the trip take, and what is her average speed (to the nearest mi./hr.)?

   26.7 min.; 56 mi./hr.

5. A bouncy ball has the property of rebounding to 80% of the distance it fell. If the ball rebounds 40.96 dm after its fourth bounce, what is the total distance it has traveled when it falls back to the surface after the fourth bounce? (Hint: The initial drop distance occurs only once, while all others occur twice.)

   572.32 dm

6. At the end of the day on Friday a grocery store has only eighteen boxes left of a popular brand of cereal. Friday was a big day, with 75% of the inventory being sold. On Thursday 20% of the inventory at that time was sold, on Wednesday eighteen boxes were sold, on Tuesday 10% was sold, and on Monday 20% of the inventory was sold. How many boxes were in the inventory at the start of Monday?

   150 boxes

Numbers That Surprise (Enrichment; use after 11.1.)

The number of properties and relationships that exist among numbers seems endless. You have seen some fascinating patterns of numbers in previous chapters. This activity looks at more surprising relationships as well as the beauty and orderliness associated with number properties.

The Principle of 22

Select a three-digit number in which all the digits are different. Now form all possible two-digit numbers from these three digits. (We know there will be six because the number of permutations of three objects taken two at a time is six.) Now divide the sum of these six numbers by the sum of the digits of the original number. The result is 22.

Example 1

Apply the principle of 22 to the three-digit number 462.

Answer

Form all possible two-digit numbers using 4, 6, and 2: 46, 64, 42, 24, 62, and 26.

Then find their sum: $46 + 64 + 42 + 24 + 62 + 26 = 264$.

Add the digits of the three-digit number: $4 + 6 + 2 = 12$.

Finally, find the quotient: $\frac{264}{12} = 22$.

Apply the principle of 22 to the following three-digit numbers.

$\frac{308}{14} = 22$ _____ 1. 365

$\frac{396}{18} = 22$ _____ 2. 198

$\frac{330}{15} = 22$ _____ 3. 285

$\frac{418}{19} = 22$ _____ 4. 964

$\frac{396}{18} = 22$ _____ 5. 549

$\frac{374}{17} = 22$ _____ 6. 728

7. To figure out how this fascinating principle works, write each two-digit number from Example 1 as the sum of two numbers (e.g., $42 = 40 + 2$). Now add all of the numbers that are made from the same digit (e.g., the 40s and 4s). The way the principle of 22 works should become apparent when you add the numbers this way.

   $40 + 40 + 4 + 4 = 88 = 4 \times 22$; $60 + 60 + 6 + 6 = 132 = 6 \times 22$; $20 + 20 + 2 + 2 = 44 = 2 \times 22$;
   $4 \times 22 + 6 \times 22 + 2 \times 22 = (4 + 6 + 2) \times 22$

Two-Digit Numbers Ending in 9

Any two-digit number ending in 9 can be written as the product of its digits plus the sum of its digits.

Example 2
Verify the above principle for 19, 29, and 39.

Answer
$(1 \cdot 9) + (1 + 9) = 9 + 10 = 19$

$(2 \cdot 9) + (2 + 9) = 18 + 11 = 29$

$(3 \cdot 9) + (3 + 9) = 27 + 12 = 39$

Complete the pattern for the next six two-digit numbers ending in 9.

8. 49
   $(4 \cdot 9) + (4 + 9) = 36 + 13 = 49$

9. 59
   $(5 \cdot 9) + (5 + 9) = 45 + 14 = 59$

10. 69
    $(6 \cdot 9) + (6 + 9) = 54 + 15 = 69$

11. 79
    $(7 \cdot 9) + (7 + 9) = 63 + 16 = 79$

12. 89
    $(8 \cdot 9) + (8 + 9) = 72 + 17 = 89$

13. 99
    $(9 \cdot 9) + (9 + 9) = 81 + 18 = 99$

The Number 1,089

Notice that $65^2 - 56^2 = 33^2 = 1,089$. This connects 1,089 to a Pythagorean triple. Additionally, the first nine multiples of 1,089 produce an interesting pattern.

14. Find the first nine nonzero multiples of 1,089 and enter them in the table below.

$1,089 \cdot 1$	1,089	$1,089 \cdot 4$	4,356	$1,089 \cdot 7$	7,623
$1,089 \cdot 2$	2,178	$1,089 \cdot 5$	5,445	$1,089 \cdot 8$	8,712
$1,089 \cdot 3$	3,267	$1,089 \cdot 6$	6,534	$1,089 \cdot 9$	9,801

15. How are the first and last multiples related? Does this pattern continue?
    They are the same digits in reverse order. Yes, the pattern continues with the second and eighth multiples, the third and seventh multiples, and the fourth and sixth multiples.

16. Insert a 9 into the number, giving 10,989. Find the first nine nonzero multiples of 10,989. Does the same pattern hold?
    Yes, the pattern holds.

17. Test the multiples of 109,989 (the result of inserting two 9s). Does the same pattern hold for the multiples of this number?
    Yes, the pattern holds.

Solving Equations Containing Radicals   (Extra Practice; use after 11.2.)

Solve and check the following equations. If no answer exists, state "no real solution." Use your calculator for numbers that are not perfect squares.

_____6,561_____ 1. $\sqrt{x} = 81$

_____256_____ 2. $3\sqrt{x} = 48$

_____2.45_____ 3. $\sqrt{5x} = 3.5$

_____18_____ 4. $8\sqrt{2x} = 48$

_____6.05_____ 5. $7\sqrt{5x} = 38.5$

_____27_____ 6. $\sqrt{3x} + 11 = 20$

_____no real solution_____ 7. $\sqrt{6x} + 32 = 16$

_____−135_____ 8. $\sqrt{9 - x} - 2.5 = 9.5$

_____66_____ 9. $\sqrt{x - 2} = 8$

_____32_____ 10. $15 - \sqrt{2x} = 7$

_____no real solution_____ 11. $\sqrt{8x} + 24 = 8$

_____20_____ 12. $16\sqrt{x + 5} = 80$

_____7_____ 13. $-6\sqrt{x - 3} + 14 = 2$

_____36_____ 14. $2\sqrt{2x - 8} = 16$

Make a Conjecture

15. What is the definition of a principal square root?
    the positive square root

16. Some of the equations in exercises 1–14 had no real number solutions. Examine those results again and make a general conjecture as to what situation resulted in no solution.
    When a square root is equal to a negative number, there is no real solution.

17. Does your conjecture from exercise 16 apply to other types of roots (e.g., cube roots, fourth roots, fifth roots, etc.)?
    It applies only to even-indexed roots.

Solving Equations Containing Exponents (Extra Practice; use after 11.3.)

Solve. Leave answers in radical form if the radicand is not a perfect square. If no answer exists, state "no real solution."

__±12__   1. $x^2 = 144$

__±7__   2. $x^2 + 31 = 80$

__±4__   3. $x^2 + 4 = 20$

__±$\sqrt{28}$__   4. $12x^2 = 336$

__no real solution__   5. $14 - 3x^2 = 20$

__±11__   6. $x^2 - 58 = 63$

__20, −12__   7. $(x - 4)^2 = 256$

__±$\sqrt{17}$__   8. $5x^2 + 13 = 98$

__no real solution__   9. $5x^2 + 45 = 20$

__10, −16__   10. $(x + 3)^2 = 169$

__4, 14__   11. $(9 - x)^2 = 25$

__±8__   12. $x^2 - 9 = 55$

__±16__   13. $6x^2 = 1{,}536$

__±1__   14. $-3x^2 + 4 = 1$

__±$\sqrt{15}$__   15. $8x^2 + 9 = 129$

__$\frac{5}{8}$, $-\frac{1}{4}$__   16. $(16x - 3)^2 + 12 = 61$

Make a Conjecture

17. Some of the equations in exercises 1–16 had no real number solutions. Examine those results again and make a general conjecture as to what situation resulted in no solution.

When a square is equal to a negative number, there is no real solution.

18. Does your conjecture from exercise 17 apply to other powers of the variable?

It applies only to even powers of the variable.

Simplifying Radicals (Extra Practice; use after 11.6.)

Simplify the following radicals.

_____$4\sqrt{3}$_____ 1. $\sqrt{48}$

_____$4\sqrt{6}$_____ 2. $\sqrt{96}$

_____$5\sqrt{5}$_____ 3. $\sqrt{125}$

_____$6\sqrt{7}$_____ 4. $\sqrt{252}$

_____$9\sqrt{5}$_____ 5. $\sqrt{405}$

_____$7\sqrt{11}$_____ 6. $\sqrt{539}$

_____$9\sqrt{7}$_____ 7. $\sqrt{567}$

_____$10\sqrt{6}$_____ 8. $\sqrt{600}$

Simplify the following radical expressions.

_____$7\sqrt{7}$_____ 9. $4\sqrt{7} - 2\sqrt{7} + 5\sqrt{7}$

_____-4_____ 10. $2\sqrt{9} - 5\sqrt{4}$

_____$6\sqrt{2}$_____ 11. $\sqrt{6} \cdot \sqrt{12}$

_____2_____ 12. $\dfrac{\sqrt{20}}{\sqrt{5}}$

_____$21\sqrt{2}$_____ 13. $\sqrt{50} + \sqrt{162} + \sqrt{98}$

_____$24\sqrt{5}$_____ 14. $2\sqrt{8} \cdot 3\sqrt{10}$

_____$2\sqrt{5}$_____ 15. $4\sqrt{5} + \sqrt{80} - 2\sqrt{45}$

_____$11\sqrt{3}$_____ 16. $\sqrt{11} \cdot \sqrt{33}$

_____$169\sqrt{6}$_____ 17. $\sqrt{169} \cdot \sqrt{26} \cdot \sqrt{39}$

_____$\dfrac{10}{3}$_____ 18. $\dfrac{5\sqrt{28}}{\sqrt{63}}$

_____$4\sqrt{5}$_____ 19. $\dfrac{2\sqrt{160}}{\sqrt{8}}$

_____0_____ 20. $\sqrt{80} - \sqrt{245} + 3\sqrt{5}$

Cube Roots   (Extra Practice; use after 11.7.)

1. Write out the cubes of the first twelve positive integers.
   1, 8, 27, 64, 125, 216, 343, 512, 729, 1,000, 1,331, 1,728

Find the consecutive integers between which the following cube roots lie.

2 and 3   2. $\sqrt[3]{25}$

3 and 4   3. $\sqrt[3]{55}$

5 and 6   4. $\sqrt[3]{180}$

−5 and −4   5. $\sqrt[3]{-100}$

6 and 7   6. $\sqrt[3]{240}$

−5 and −4   7. $\sqrt[3]{-80}$

Find the following cube roots.

−2   8. $\sqrt[3]{-8}$

1.5   9. $\sqrt[3]{3.375}$

$\frac{1}{2}$ 10. $\sqrt[3]{\frac{1}{8}}$

100   11. $\sqrt[3]{10^6}$

−8   12. $\sqrt[3]{-512}$

$\frac{3}{4}$ 13. $\sqrt[3]{\frac{27}{64}}$

Estimate the following cube roots to the nearest tenth.

2.9   14. $\sqrt[3]{25}$

3.8   15. $\sqrt[3]{55}$

5.6   16. $\sqrt[3]{180}$

−4.6   17. $\sqrt[3]{-100}$

6.2   18. $\sqrt[3]{240}$

−4.3   19. $\sqrt[3]{-80}$

Simplify the following cube roots.

$2\sqrt[3]{3}$ 20. $\sqrt[3]{24}$

$3\sqrt[3]{3}$ 21. $\sqrt[3]{81}$

$5\sqrt[3]{7}$ 22. $\sqrt[3]{875}$

$-2\sqrt[3]{9}$ 23. $\sqrt[3]{-72}$

$6\sqrt[3]{6}$ 24. $\sqrt[3]{1,296}$

$-4\sqrt[3]{15}$ 25. $\sqrt[3]{-960}$

Calculator Skill 11 (Use after 11.7.)

written for the TI-30Xa

Extracting Roots

The calculator has several root keys. The square root function key, $\boxed{\sqrt{x}}$, calculates square roots. The cube root function key, $\boxed{\sqrt[3]{x}}$ ($\boxed{\text{2nd}}$ 0) calculates cube roots. Other roots can be found using the second function of the $\boxed{y^x}$ key. This is the $\boxed{\sqrt[x]{y}}$ key, where x is the root (index) and y is the radicand.

Example 1
Calculate $\sqrt[6]{64}$.

Answer
Keystrokes: 64 $\boxed{\sqrt[x]{y}}$ ($\boxed{\text{2nd}}$ $\boxed{y^x}$) 6 $\boxed{=}$

Result: 2

Example 2
Calculate $\sqrt[4]{2}$.

Answer
Keystrokes: 2 $\boxed{\sqrt[x]{y}}$ ($\boxed{\text{2nd}}$ $\boxed{y^x}$) 4 $\boxed{=}$

Result: 1.189207115

Use your calculator to perform the following calculations.

_1.414213562_	1. $\sqrt{2}$	
_1.732050808_	3. $\sqrt{3}$	
_2.080083823_	5. $\sqrt[6]{81}$	
_2.236067978_	7. $\sqrt{5}$	
_2.203944575_	9. $\sqrt[5]{5^2 + 3^3}$	
_3.602810866_	11. $\sqrt[3]{9} \cdot \sqrt[6]{9} \cdot \sqrt[12]{9}$	
_1.617442799_	13. $\sqrt{1 + \sqrt{1 + \sqrt{1 + \sqrt{1 + \sqrt{1 + \sqrt{2}}}}}}$	
_1.618033989_	14. $\dfrac{1 + \sqrt{5}}{2}$	

_1.414213562_	2. $\sqrt[4]{4}$	
_1.732050808_	4. $\sqrt[4]{9}$	
_2.236067978_	6. $\sqrt[3]{5} \cdot \sqrt[6]{5}$	
_1.709975947_	8. $\sqrt[6]{25}$	
_10_	10. $\sqrt{\sqrt{10^4}}$	
_3.602810866_	12. $\sqrt[6]{3^7}$	

The fraction in exercise 14 is the golden ratio. The nested square roots in exercise 13 give an interesting approximation for the golden ratio. It will get more accurate if you expand it further.

© BJU Press. Reproduction prohibited.

Chapter 11 Review

Write T for true or F for false. If the statement is false, correct it or give an example showing why it is false.

__T__ 1. Each positive number has two square roots.

__T__ 2. An irrational number is a nonterminating, nonrepeating decimal.

__F__ 3. All square roots are irrational numbers.
$\sqrt{4} = 2$ is rational

__T__ 4. Subtracting two radicals requires the radicals to have the same radicand.

Find the following roots.

__9__ 5. $\sqrt{81}$

__−14__ 6. $-\sqrt{196}$

__12__ 7. $\sqrt{144}$

__7__ 8. $\sqrt{49}$

__−3__ 9. $\sqrt[3]{-27}$

__7__ 10. $\sqrt[3]{343}$

Simplify the following radical expressions.

__8__ 11. $\sqrt{19 + 45}$

__2__ 12. $\sqrt{36} - \sqrt{16}$

__15__ 13. $2\sqrt{9} + \sqrt{81}$

__6__ 14. $\sqrt{100 - 64}$

__2__ 15. $\dfrac{\sqrt{12}}{\sqrt{3}}$

__$\frac{9}{10}$__ 16. $\sqrt{\dfrac{81}{100}}$

Estimate the following roots to the nearest integer.

__5__ 17. $\sqrt{28}$

__−9__ 18. $-\sqrt{82}$

__4__ 19. $\sqrt[3]{79}$

__−5__ 20. $\sqrt[3]{-115}$

Estimate the following square roots to the nearest tenth.

__9.7__ 21. $\sqrt{94}$

__11.4__ 22. $\sqrt{129}$

Solve.

_____144_____ 23. $\sqrt{x} = 12$

_____18_____ 24. $\sqrt{8x} = 12$

_____15_____ 25. $\sqrt{2x + 6} = 6$

_____±9_____ 26. $x^2 = 81$

_____±7_____ 27. $5x^2 = 245$

_____±13_____ 28. $x^2 + 8 = 177$

Find the length of the missing side.

_____15_____ 29.

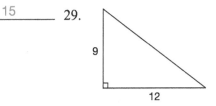

_____12_____ 30.

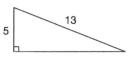

31. A stick 2 ft. tall casts a shadow 10 ft. long. If a proportion exists between the ratio of the height of the stick to its shadow and the height of a tree to its shadow, how long would be the shadow of a 40 ft. tree?
200 ft.

32. An extension ladder is set at a length of 11 ft. and is leaning against a wall. The base of the ladder is 3 ft. from the wall. Find how high up the ladder reaches on the wall (to the nearest tenth of a foot).
10.6 ft.

Simplify the following radical expressions.

_____$3\sqrt{22}$_____ 33. $\sqrt{198}$

_____4_____ 34. $\dfrac{\sqrt{32}}{\sqrt{2}}$

_____$3\sqrt{15}$_____ 35. $\sqrt{3} \cdot \sqrt{45}$

_____$84\sqrt{2}$_____ 36. $4\sqrt{7} \cdot 3\sqrt{14}$

_____$-2\sqrt{2} + 5\sqrt{3}$_____ 37. $\sqrt{72} + \sqrt{75} - \sqrt{128}$

_____$3\sqrt[3]{25}$_____ 38. $\sqrt[3]{675}$

_____$-3\sqrt[3]{7}$_____ 39. $\sqrt[3]{56} - \sqrt[3]{875}$

_____4_____ 40. $\sqrt[3]{16} \cdot \sqrt[3]{4}$

Cumulative Review 11

_____c_____ 1. $\sqrt{8}$ is a member of which set of numbers? (State the most inclusive set.)
    a. whole   d. rationals
    b. integers   e. none of these
    c. real

_____c_____ 2. Which of the following characterizes $\frac{7}{9}$ when it is converted to decimal form?
    a. terminating   d. nonrepeating
    b. periodic   e. none of these
    c. repeating

_____e_____ 3. Solve $9(a - 7) + 3a = 4a - 119$.
    a. -56 d. $22\frac{3}{4}$
    b. $-\frac{69}{4}$ e. none of these
    c. $-\frac{7}{2}$

_____a_____ 4. Multiply $(2.6 \times 10^8) \cdot (1.2 \times 10^{14})$.
    a. 3.12×10^{22} d. 3.8×10^6
    b. 3.8×10^{22} e. none of these
    c. 31.2×10^{21}

_____d_____ 5. What number is 38% of 280?
    a. 10,640   d. 106.4
    b. 736.84   e. none of these
    c. 7.36

_____c_____ 6. Write 4.58 as a percent.
    a. 45.8%   d. 0.458%
    b. 0.0458%   e. none of these
    c. 458%

_____b_____ 7. Solve $4y - 19 > -16$.
    a. $y > -\frac{35}{4}$ d. $y < -\frac{35}{4}$
    b. $y > \frac{3}{4}$ e. none of these
    c. $y < 4$

_____b_____ 8. The ordered pair $(-7, 2)$ is in which quadrant on a coordinate plane?
    a. I   d. on an axis
    b. II   e. none of these
    c. III

<u> c </u> 9. Find the slope of the line passing through points (6, 10) and (−1, 4).

    a. $\frac{6}{5}$ d. $\frac{4}{5}$

    b. $\frac{7}{6}$ e. none of these

    c. $\frac{6}{7}$

<u> d </u> 10. If y varies directly with x and $y = 12$ when $x = 4$, find y when $x = 15$.

    a. 5   d. 45

    b. 48   e. none of these

    c. 180

<u> b </u> 11. Find the slope and y-intercept of the line $3x − y = 14$.

    a. $m = −3$; (0, −14)   d. $m = \frac{14}{3}$; (0, 14)

    b. $m = 3$; (0, −14)   e. none of these

    c. $m = 3$; (0, 14)

<u> a </u> 12. Evaluate $_8P_2$.

    a. 56   d. 6

    b. 28   e. none of these

    c. 40,320

<u> a </u> 13. If three quarters are flipped at the same time, what is the probability of getting all heads?

    a. $\frac{1}{8}$ d. 3

    b. $\frac{1}{3}$ e. none of these

    c. $\frac{1}{2}$

<u> d </u> 14. If there are twelve children in the first-grade class, how many ways can six of them be chosen to go to recess first?

    a. 1,848   d. 924

    b. 72   e. none of these

    c. 665,280

<u> b </u> 15. Which of the following relations is a function?

    a. {3, 5, 1, 9}   d. {(1, 1), (2, 2), (3, 3), (3, 2)}

    b. {(3, −7), (6, 7), (2, −7), (5, 3)}   e. none of these

    c. {(4, 7), (3, −2), (4, 8), (1, 6)}

Figurate Numbers (Enrichment; use after 12.1.)

Figurate numbers are integers that can be represented by an array of dots in a regular polygonal arrangement. Most mathematicians would also accept numbers that form oblong figures (such as rectangles) as legitimate figurate numbers, even though they form a rectangle rather than a regular polygon.

Examine the first four figures and give the first four integers (number of dots used) in the array of numbers. Draw the next figure and tell how many dots were used.

1. triangular
   1, 3, 6, 10; 15

2. square
   1, 4, 9, 16; 25

3. oblong
   2, 6, 12, 20; 30

4. pentagonal
   1, 5, 12, 22; 35

Find an algebraic expression that could be used to find the number of dots for each type of figurate number above. Use this expression to find the tenth number in the array.

$\frac{n}{2}(n + 1)$; 55 _____ 5. triangular n^2; 100 _____ 6. square

$n(n + 1)$; 110 _____ 7. oblong $\frac{n}{2}(3n - 1)$; 145 _____ 8. pentagonal

9. Observe the sequence of numbers and tell how the triangular numbers are related to the square numbers.
   $T_1 + T_2 = S_2$; $T_2 + T_3 = S_3$; ...; $T_n + T_{n+1} = S_{n+1}$

10. Now tell how the triangular numbers are related to the oblong numbers.
    $2T_1 = O_1$; $2T_2 = O_2$; ...; $2T_n = O_n$

11. How is the sum of the oblong numbers and the square numbers related to the triangular numbers?
    $S_1 + O_1 = T_2$; $S_2 + O_2 = T_4$; $S_3 + O_3 = T_6$; ...; $S_n + O_n = T_{2n}$

12. Draw the first four terms of the hexagonal numbers. Find a pattern and write an algebraic expression for the pattern; then find the tenth number in the array.
    $n(2n - 1)$; 190

Angles (Extra Practice; use after 12.2.)

Find the complement and supplement of the following angles. If an angle has no complement or supplement, write "none."

<u>45°; 135°</u>   1. 45°

<u>26°; 116°</u>   2. 64°

<u>none; 42°</u>   3. 138°

<u>none; none</u>   4. 180°

<u>78°; 168°</u>   5. 12°

<u>4°; 94°</u>   6. 86°

Using the given figure, identify each pair of angles as adjacent, alternate exterior, alternate interior, corresponding, or vertical.

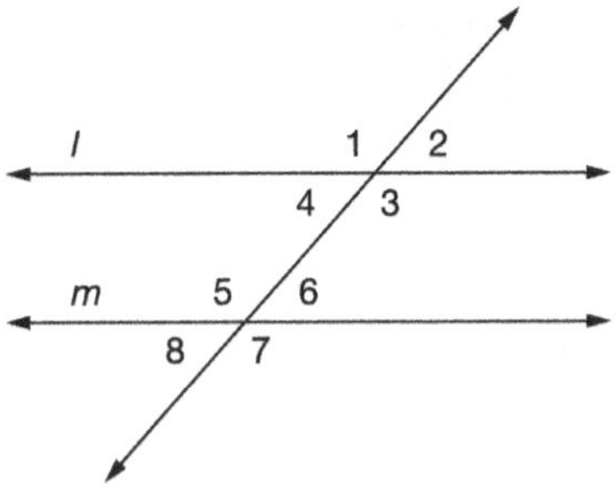

<u>vertical</u>   7. ∠1 and ∠3

<u>alternate interior</u>   8. ∠4 and ∠6

<u>alternate exterior</u>   9. ∠2 and ∠8

<u>corresponding</u>   10. ∠2 and ∠6

<u>adjacent</u>   11. ∠2 and ∠3

<u>corresponding</u>   12. ∠4 and ∠8

In the figure above, $l \parallel m$ and $m\angle 1 = 120°$. Find the measure of the following angles.

<u>60°</u>   13. $m\angle 2$

<u>120°</u>   14. $m\angle 3$

<u>60°</u>   15. $m\angle 4$

<u>120°</u>   16. $m\angle 5$

<u>60°</u>   17. $m\angle 6$

<u>120°</u>   18. $m\angle 7$

<u>60°</u>   19. $m\angle 8$

Geometric Proofs (Enrichment; use after 12.2.)

Prove the following statements. Supply the reasons in the first and third proofs and both the statements and the reasons in the second proof.

1. Prove: Vertical angles have the same measure ($m\angle 1 = m\angle 3$).

Statement	Reason
1. $\angle 1$ and $\angle 3$ are vertical angles.	1. definition of vertical angles
2. $\angle 1$ and $\angle 2$ are supplementary.	2. Two angles that form a straight line are supplementary.
3. $m\angle 1 + m\angle 2 = 180°$	3. definition of supplementary angles
4. $\angle 2$ and $\angle 3$ are supplementary.	4. Two angles that form a straight line are supplementary.
5. $m\angle 2 + m\angle 3 = 180°$	5. definition of supplementary angles
6. $m\angle 1 + m\angle 2 = m\angle 2 + m\angle 3$	6. substitution (step 5 into step 3)
7. $m\angle 1 = m\angle 3$	7. Addition Property of Equality ($m\angle 2$ subtracted from both sides)

2. Given: $m\angle 1 = m\angle 2$.
   Prove: $\angle 2$ and $\angle 4$ are supplementary.

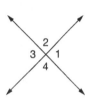

Statement	Reason
1. $m\angle 1 = m\angle 2$	1. given
2. $\angle 1$ and $\angle 4$ are supplementary.	2. Two angles that form a straight line are supplementary.
3. $m\angle 1 + m\angle 4 = 180°$	3. definition of supplementary angles
4. $m\angle 2 + m\angle 4 = 180°$	4. substitution (step 1 into step 3)
5. $\angle 2$ and $\angle 4$ are supplementary.	5. definition of supplementary angles

3. Given: $m\angle BAC = m\angle DAE$.
   Prove: $m\angle BAD = m\angle CAE$.

Statement	Reason
1. $m\angle BAC = m\angle DAE$	1. given
2. $m\angle BAC + m\angle CAD = m\angle DAE + m\angle CAD$	2. Addition Property of Equality
3. $m\angle BAC + m\angle CAD = m\angle BAD$ $m\angle DAE + m\angle CAD = m\angle CAE$	3. angle addition
4. $m\angle BAD = m\angle CAE$	4. substitution (step 3 into step 2)

Problem Solving—Tables and Venn Diagrams (Use after 12.3.)

Use a table, a list, or a Venn diagram to help you solve the following problems.

1. Four young men named Randal, Robert, Nadal, and Norman have summer jobs that involve mowing yards, stocking grocery shelves, delivering pizza, and caddying golf. Randal has grass allergies and cannot drive; Robert and Nadal both like working outdoors in the sunshine and fresh air. Nadal and Norman make all their money in tips. Identify the summer job for each one.
   Randal stocks grocery shelves, Robert mows, Nadal caddies, and Norman delivers pizza.

2. Of the 76 juniors and seniors at the Answersstone Charter School for Science and Technology, 45 are taking pre-calculus, 16 are taking astronomy, and 38 are taking physics. Only two of the astronomy students are taking physics and not pre-calculus. Thirty of the pre-calculus students are not taking physics. Six astronomy students are also taking pre-calculus, and three students are taking all three subjects. How many are taking just physics, and how many are taking just astronomy?
   physics only: 21; astronomy only: 8

3. Match the summer recreation choices of swimming, backpacking, horseback riding, and playing tennis with the four girls Rachel, Rebecca, Leah, and Sarah. Rachel's sport requires the least amount of equipment. Rebecca's and Leah's recreation choices do not require a ball of any kind. Sarah cannot tolerate mosquitoes or flies. Leah is allergic to horses.
   Rachel swims, Rebecca rides horses, Leah backpacks, and Sarah plays tennis.

4. The Conners twins, Angela and Megan, and the Ricardo twins, Felipe and Luis, all have favorite baseball teams: the Boston Red Sox, the Cleveland Indians, the Atlanta Braves, and the San Francisco Giants. Angela and Megan like teams with Native American mascots, while Felipe and Luis like teams on the opposite coasts of the US. The Ricardo family lives in Charleston, SC, while the Conners family lives in Fairfax, VA. Luis sometimes gets in trouble for staying up late to watch his team play a night-game home stand. Megan's team has always played in its current city. (This last clue may require some research.)
   Angela likes the Braves, Megan likes the Indians, Felipe likes the Red Sox, and Luis likes the Giants.

5. Two copier companies have different monthly rental charges and costs per copy. DigiPrint charges \$500/mo. and \$0.05/copy, while ReproPrint charges \$350/mo. and \$0.07/copy. Set up a table using thousands of copies between 5,000 and 15,000 and find the number of copies that determines which copier is less expensive to rent.
   DigiPrint is better for greater than 7,500 copies, and ReproPrint is better for fewer than 7,500 copies.

Calculator Skill 12 (Use after 12.3.)

written for the TI-30Xa

Angles of Regular Polygons

Remember that regular polygons have all sides congruent and all angles congruent. A regular 3-gon is an equilateral triangle, and a regular 4-gon is a square. Review the prefixes for the 5-gon through the 12-gon in Section 12.3 of the student text.

Find the sum of the measures of the angles and then the measure of each angle in the following regular polygons. Round to the nearest hundredth if necessary.

_720°; 120°_   1. hexagon   _900°; 128.57°_   2. heptagon

_1,080°; 135°_   3. octagon   _1,260°; 140°_   4. nonagon

_1,440°; 144°_   5. decagon   _1,800°; 150°_   6. dodecagon

_3,240°; 162°_   7. 20-gon   _8,640°; 172.8°_   8. 50-gon

_17,640°; 176.4°_   9. 100-gon   _179,640°; 179.64°_   10. 1,000-gon

11. What do you notice about the measure of an angle as the number of sides increases?

    The measure of an angle increases as the number of sides increases, but it seems that it will not exceed 180°.

12. Make a conjecture about the angles of an _n_-gon as _n_ increases.

    As the number of sides increases, the measure of each interior angle gets closer and closer to 180°.

Since the sum of the angles is $(n - 2)180°$, the formula $A = \dfrac{(n-2)180}{n}$ can be used to find the measure of each interior angle of a regular _n_-gon. When this formula is solved for _n_, a new formula results. The formula $n = \dfrac{360}{180 - A}$, where _A_ is the measure of each interior angle, can be used to find the number of sides in a regular _n_-gon.

Given the measure of an angle, find the number of sides for each regular polygon.

_30_   13. 168°   _64_   14. 174.375°

_15,000_   15. 179.976°   _11_   16. $147.\overline{27}°$

Creation Wonders—The Human Brain (Bible Activity; use after 12.4.)

Of all the organs and systems in the human body, the brain is the least understood; in fact, many scientists see it as the most complex physical structure existing anywhere in the universe. Nothing about us shows more evidence of the image of God in us than does the brain. It controls every function of the human body; yet that level of chemical-electrical control pales next to our ability to speak, to remember, to reason, to sense emotion, or to create both abstractly and concretely.

The vast variety of human languages can be learned almost passively by any child through the use of this God-given computer—the brain. Placed in the right conditions, a child can learn multiple languages simultaneously and never confuse the use of any one of them. One educator related a situation in which a three-year-old boy talked to three people—one spoke German, one spoke French, and one spoke English—in each of their languages with absolutely seamless transitions between the various languages.

However, very little is understood of how linguistic information is processed or stored. Scans of the brain have revealed places in which certain functions originate and how functions are divided between the right and left sides or between the back, middle, and front sections of the brain. We know that the brain contains about 8.5×10^{10} nerve cells called *neurons*. The brain also contains 10^{12} other cells that handle metabolic functions and structural support. The connecting links between neurons are called *synapses*. Because of the number of links needed between neurons, the number of synapses is considerably larger than the number of neurons—between 20 and 100,000 connections per neuron. The length of nerve fibers required to make these connections exceeds 10^9 m—or roughly three times the distance from the earth to the moon. Surely the creation of the human brain teaches us about the greatness and majesty of the Creator.

1. Modern computer processor speeds are given in gigahertz, or 10^9 cycles per second. It has been estimated that the incredibly dense neuronal network of the brain can do 10^{18} calculations per second. How many gigahertz is the processing speed of a computer that is capable of the same number of calculations per second?

   10^9, or one billion gigahertz

2. With the number of connections per neuron being between 20 and 100,000, how many total connections would we expect in the human brain?

   1.7×10^{12} to 8.5×10^{15}

3. The word "mind" as used in Scripture has a variety of meanings, among which are the will, the intellect, the soul, the spirit, and the thoughts of a person. Use a concordance to decide which of these meanings best fits the use of the word *mind* in Romans 8:27.

   The Greek word *phronēma* refers to the will or thoughts in this context.

4. Again using a concordance, decide how *mind* is used in Ezekiel 38:10.

   The Hebrew word *lebab* refers to the intellect or thoughts in this context.

For who hath known the mind of the Lord? or who hath been his counsellor? Or who hath first given to him, and it shall be recompensed unto him again? For of him, and through him, and to him, are all things: to whom be glory for ever. Romans 11:34–36

Congruence and Similarity (Extra Practice; use after 12.5.)

△*ABC* ≅ △*DEF*. **Complete each statement.**

_____ $\overline{DE}$ _____   1. $\overline{AB} \cong$ ___

_____ $\overline{AC}$ _____   2. $\overline{DF} \cong$ ___

_____ $\overline{EF}$ _____   3. $\overline{BC} \cong$ ___

_____ $\angle D$ _____   4. $\angle A \cong$ ___

_____ $\angle C$ _____   5. $\angle F \cong$ ___

_____ $\angle E$ _____   6. $\angle B \cong$ ___

△*PQR* ~ △*STV*. **Complete each statement.**

_____ $\angle S$ _____   7. $\angle P \cong$ ___

_____ $\angle Q$ _____   8. $\angle T \cong$ ___

_____ $\angle V$ _____   9. $\angle R \cong$ ___

_____ TV _____   10. $\dfrac{PQ}{ST} = \dfrac{QR}{?}$

_____ PQ _____   11. $\dfrac{PR}{SV} = \dfrac{?}{ST}$

_____ QR _____   12. $\dfrac{PR}{?} = \dfrac{SV}{TV}$

Write a congruence or similarity statement for each pair of triangles.

_____ $\triangle ABC \cong \triangle JKH$ _____ 13.

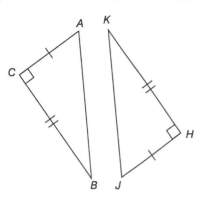

_____ $\triangle MNO \sim \triangle QPO$ _____ 14.

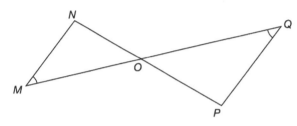

Use proportions to find the missing lengths. Remember that corresponding sides lie opposite congruent angles.

_____ $x = 12$ _____ 15.

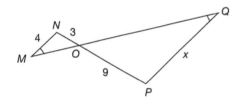

_____ $y = 24$ _____ 16.

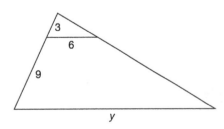

Special Triangles (Extra Practice; use after 12.6.)

Find the unknown lengths in the following 45-45 and 30-60 right triangles.

_____a = 5, c = 10_____ 1.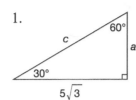

_____a = 6, c = 6√2_____ 2.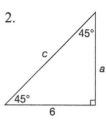

_____a = 6, b = 6√3_____ 3.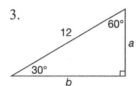

_____b = 8√3, c = 16_____ 4.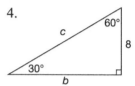

_____a = 10, b = 10_____ 5.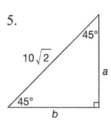

_____a = √3, c = √6_____ 6.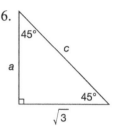

_____a = 6, b = 6√3_____ 7.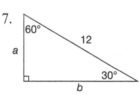

_____b = √6, c = 2√2_____ 8.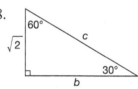

_____a = 18, b = 18_____ 9.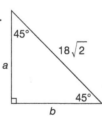

_____a = 6, c = 12_____ 10.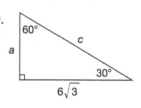

_____5√2 m_____ 11. What is the length of the diagonal of a square with sides of 5 m?

_____5√3 m_____ 12. What is the length of the diagonal of a cube measuring 5 m on a side?

_____6√3 cm_____ 13. What is the height of an equilateral triangle whose side is 12 cm? (Hint: Each angle of an equilateral triangle measures 60°.)

14. The diagonal of a rectangle forms two congruent 30-60 triangles. If the width of the rectangle is 9√3 in., what is the length of the rectangle and the measure of the diagonal?
    length = 27 in., diagonal = 18√3 in.

15. A pup tent makes an angle with the ground of 60°. If the height of the tent at its highest point is 4 ft., what is the width of the tent? (Use a calculator to approximate the width to the nearest tenth of a foot.)
    4.6 ft.

Coordinate Geometry—Distance and Midpoint (Extra Practice; use after 12.7.)

Given the coordinates of two points, find the distance between the points and the midpoint of the segment defined by the points. Leave distances in simplified radical form.

$d = 3; \left(\frac{7}{2}, 1\right)$ 1. A (2, 1), B (5, 1)

$d = 10; (3, 0)$ 2. P (3, –5), Q (3, 5)

$d = 2\sqrt{13}; (–1, 1)$ 3. C (2, –1), D (–4, 3)

$d = 2\sqrt{41}; (1, 3)$ 4. W (–3, –2), Z (5, 8)

$d = 13; \left(1, \frac{11}{2}\right)$ 5. X (7, 8), Y (–5, 3)

$d = 10; (6, 1)$ 6. A (10, 4), B (2, –2)

$d = 17; \left(-\frac{9}{2}, 2\right)$ 7. P (–12, –2), Q (3, 6)

$d = 2\sqrt{145}; (2, 4)$ 8. C (3, 16), D (1, –8)

$d = 53; \left(-\frac{5}{2}, 6\right)$ 9. W (20, 20), Z (–25, –8)

$d = 25; \left(-\frac{1}{2}, -4\right)$ 10. X (–4, –16), Y (3, 8)

$d = 2\sqrt{29}; (0, 0)$ 11. R (5, –2), T (–5, 2)

$d = 2\sqrt{2}; \left(-\frac{1}{2}, \frac{3}{8}\right)$ 12. K $\left(\frac{1}{2}, -\frac{5}{8}\right)$, M $\left(-\frac{3}{2}, 1\frac{3}{8}\right)$

13. Given $\triangle ABC$ with vertices A (2, –5), B (6, 3), and C (8, –1), find the length of the sides of the triangle.
    $AB = 4\sqrt{5}$; $AC = 2\sqrt{13}$; $BC = 2\sqrt{5}$

14. Find the midpoints of the sides of $\triangle ABC$ in exercise 13.
    midpoint of AB = (4, –1); midpoint of AC = (5, –3); midpoint of BC = (7, 1)

15. The medians of a triangle are segments joining a vertex to the midpoint of the opposite side. Find the lengths of the medians of $\triangle ABC$ in exercise 13.
    median from C = 4; median from B = $\sqrt{37}$; median from A = $\sqrt{61}$

16. Given quadrilateral $PQRS$ with vertices P (2, 5), Q (12, 9), R (10, 3), and S (4, –3), find the midpoints of the sides of the quadrilateral.
    midpoint of PQ = (7, 7); midpoint of PS = (3, 1); midpoint of QR = (11, 6); midpoint of RS = (7, 0)

Chapter 12 Review

Use the figure to answer exercises 1–10.

_AB̄, BC̄, or BĒ_   1. Name two segments with endpoint *B*.

∠ABE or ∠CBE   2. Name a right angle.

∠GED, ∠BEG, ∠BED, or ∠FEH   3. Name an acute angle.

_AC⃡ ⊥ BE⃡_   4. Name two perpendicular lines.

_ED⃗, EG⃗, EB⃗, EF⃗, or EH⃗_   5. Name two rays with endpoint *E*.

∠GEF or ∠DEH   6. ∠*GED* and ___ are supplementary angles.

∠FEH   7. ∠*GED* and ___ are vertical angles.

∠GEF, ∠FEB, ∠HEB, or ∠DEH   8. Name an obtuse angle.

∠ABC, ∠DEF, or ∠GEH   9. Name a straight angle.

_E_   10. Name the vertex of ∠*GED*.

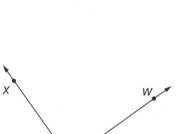

Use the figure to answer exercise 11.

m∠XYW + 39 = 117; 78°   11. *m∠XYZ* = 117°. Write and solve an equation to find *m∠XYW* if *m∠WYZ* = 39°.

_39°_   12. Find the complement of a 51° angle.

Use the figure to answer exercises 13–15. Assume that AB⃡ ∥ CD⃡.

_67°_   13. Find *m∠1*.

_67°_   14. Find *m∠2*.

_90°_   15. Find *m∠3*.

Use the figure of parallel lines cut by a transversal to answer exercises 16–21.

_____143°_____ 16. Find $m\angle 7$.

_____37°_____ 17. Find $m\angle 6$.

_____$\angle 6$_____ 18. $\angle 2$ and ___ are alternate interior angles.

_____$\angle 8$_____ 19. $\angle 6$ and ___ are corresponding angles.

_____$\angle 5$_____ 20. $\angle 1$ and ___ are alternate exterior angles.

_____$\angle 3$_____ 21. $\angle 1$ and ___ are corresponding angles.

_____equal_____ 22. When you compare a pair of corresponding, alternate interior, or alternate exterior angles formed on parallel lines, you will find that their measures are what?

Classify the following triangles according to the measures of their angles and the lengths of their sides.

_____right scalene_____ 23. All sides are of different lengths, and it contains a 90° angle.

_____obtuse isosceles_____ 24. Two sides are of the same length, and it contains a 100° angle.

Write and solve an equation to find the value of _x_.

25. _____$85 + 32 + x = 180; x = 63°$_____

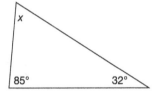

26. _____$x + 2x + 2x = 180; x = 36°$_____

_____720°_____ 27. Find the sum of the measures of the angles in a regular hexagon.

_____120°_____ 28. Find the measure of each angle in a regular hexagon.

Name the figure and find its perimeter.

29. _____quadrilateral; 29_____

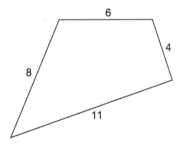

30. _____octagon; 72_____

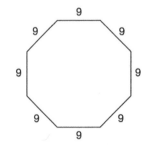

Find the circumference of the following circles. Use 3.14 for π.

_____10.048 in._____ 31. diameter of 3.2 in.   _____12.56 cm_____ 32. radius of 2 cm

△MNO ≅ △PQR. Complete each statement.

_____∠Q_____ 33. ∠N ≅ ___   _____∠R_____ 34. ∠O ≅ ___   _____$\overline{PQ}$_____ 35. $\overline{MN}$ ≅ ___

△ABC ~ △LMN. Use a proportion to find the following.

_____36_____ 36. CB if LM = 2, NM = 9, and AB = 8

Find the unknown lengths in the following special right triangles.

37. _____a = 4, c = 8_____

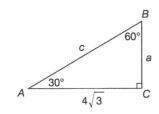

38. _____a = 4, b = 4_____

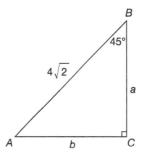

Given the coordinates of two points, find the distance between the points and the midpoint of the segment defined by the points. Leave distances in simplified radical form.

_____$d = 4\sqrt{13}; (2, -2)$_____ 39. A (6, –8), B (–2, 4)

_____$d = \sqrt{85}; \left(-\frac{1}{2}, 4\right)$_____ 40. A (3, 7), B (–4, 1)

Give the coordinates of the segment endpoints after the transformation.

_____P′ (2, 1); Q′ (–3, 3)_____ 41. reflection of the segment with endpoints P (–2, 1) and Q (3, 3) across the y-axis

_____P′ (1, 2), Q′ (3, –3)_____ 42. a 90° rotation of the segment with endpoints P (–2, 1) and Q (3, 3) around the origin

Which kinds of symmetry do the following figures have?

43. _____line, rotational, point_____

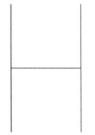

44. _____line_____

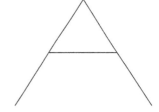

Cumulative Review 12

___b___ 1. If 6 less than twice a number is 2, find the number.
  a. 5
  b. 4
  c. −4
  d. 7
  e. none of these

___c___ 2. Multiply $\frac{5}{9} \cdot \frac{3}{25}$.
  a. $\frac{8}{34}$
  b. $\frac{125}{27}$
  c. $\frac{1}{15}$
  d. $\frac{1}{12}$
  e. none of these

___e___ 3. Evaluate $-4x + 3x^2 - 9$ when $x = -7$.
  a. −128
  b. 110
  c. −100
  d. 184
  e. none of these

___a___ 4. Simplify $9(a + 7) - 3(2a - 6)$.
  a. $3a + 81$
  b. $3a + 1$
  c. $3a + 13$
  d. $3a + 45$
  e. none of these

___d___ 5. Jessica sees a dress that originally cost $121.50 marked at 70% off. What are the discount and the sale price?
  a. $36.45; $157.95
  b. $36.45; $85.05
  c. $85.05; $206.55
  d. $85.05; $36.45
  e. none of these

___b___ 6. How much simple interest is owed on a loan of $7,000 at 8% for 3 yr.?
  a. $560
  b. $1,680
  c. $8,680
  d. $21,000
  e. none of these

___a___ 7. The manager of the sporting goods store marks up items 20% over the cost. If a soccer ball costs him $24.99, what is the retail price of the ball?
  a. $29.99
  b. $30.99
  c. $35.99
  d. $19.99
  e. none of these

___d___ 8. Solve $4y + 9 = 2(y - 6) + 69$.
  a. 27
  b. 33
  c. 36
  d. 24
  e. none of these

_____b_____ 9. Zach has $22 in his account to spend on prizes for the Bible club children. He finds small rubber balls for $0.25 each and miniature slinkies for $0.55 each. If he buys twenty slinkies and has to pay 6% sales tax, how many rubber balls can he purchase?

    a. 42   d. 44

    b. 39   e. none of these

    c. 41

_____a_____ 10. To graph $y = \frac{-3}{5}x + 2$, you should start at the origin, find two dots as follows, and connect them to form a line.

    a. Place a dot up 2; from there move down 3 and right 5 for the second dot.

    b. Place a dot down 2; from there move up 3 and right 5 for the second dot.

    c. Place a dot at the origin; move up 2 and right 5 for the second dot.

    d. Place a dot up 2; from there move left 3 and up 5 for the second dot.

    e. none of these

_____e_____ 11. How many different sandwiches, with one of each of the following, can be made from six choices of meat, four types of cheese, and three different condiments?

    a. 24   d. 216

    b. 18   e. none of these

    c. 36

_____c_____ 12. Which of the following statistical diagrams or graphs displays the minimum, maximum, first and third quartiles, and the median?

    a. histogram   d. stem-and-leaf diagram

    b. pie chart   e. none of these

    c. box-and-whisker diagram

_____c_____ 13. What is the median of {11, 8, 4, 14, 11, 9}?

    a. 11   d. 9

    b. 9.5   e. none of these

    c. 10

_____b_____ 14. Estimate $\sqrt{85}$ to the nearest integer.

    a. 8   d. 7

    b. 9   e. none of these

    c. 10

_____d_____ 15. Solve $\sqrt{b} + 10 = 18$.

    a. $4\sqrt{2}$ d. 64

    b. 8   e. none of these

    c. 784

13 Area and Volume

Areas of Rectangles, Parallelograms, Triangles, and Trapezoids (Extra Practice; use after 13.2.)

Find the area of the following figures.

1. _____ 7.84 cm² _____

2. _____ 0.98 cm² _____

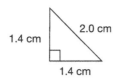

3. _____ 693 cm² _____

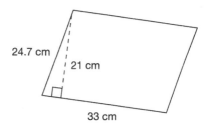

4. _____ 25.2 cm² _____

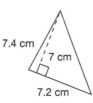

5. _____ 4.76 in.² _____

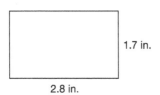

6. _____ 6.615 mm² _____

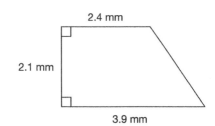

7. _____29.9 m²_____

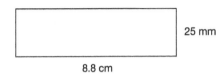

6.5 m

4.6 m

6.5 m

8. _____22 cm² or 2,200 mm²_____

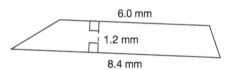

25 mm

8.8 cm

9. _____2,304 in.²_____

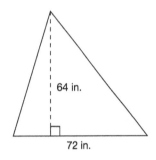

64 in.

72 in.

10. _____8.64 mm²_____

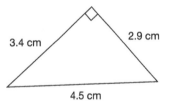

6.0 mm

1.2 mm

8.4 mm

11. _____4.93 cm²_____

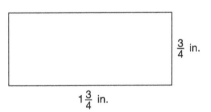

3.4 cm

2.9 cm

4.5 cm

12. _____$1\frac{5}{16}$ in.²_____

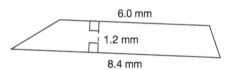

$\frac{3}{4}$ in.

$1\frac{3}{4}$ in.

13. _____5.865 cm²_____

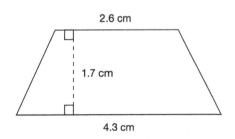

2.6 cm

1.7 cm

4.3 cm

Creation Wonders—Human Blood (Bible Activity; use after 13.6.)

The 100 trillion (10^{14}) cells in the human body all need nutrients and oxygen on a continual basis, so the Creator has designed the blood as a universal transport medium to keep all these cells functioning properly. As blood is pumped to and from the cells, it performs numerous complex functions. Besides delivering oxygen and nutrients, the blood also carries away waste products, maintains precise concentrations of various substances, regulates body temperature, and distributes hormones such as adrenalin and insulin. The blood also contains defense mechanisms: the white blood cells, which fight infection and repair damage, and the platelets, which provide the means of coagulation to stop loss of blood from wounds.

In every drop of blood there are 250 million red blood cells, each with a life span of around 120 days. During that brief time they use hemoglobin to absorb oxygen and discharge carbon dioxide 175,000 times. The red blood cells do not have a cellular nucleus, so they do not replicate themselves; rather, they are produced by the bone marrow. And the production rate is phenomenal—230 billion per day, 160 million per minute, and 2.7 million per second. The hemoglobin molecule, consisting of 10,000 atoms, can carry 70 times more oxygen than could be dissolved in the blood. The omnipotent Creator does not want us to miss His handiwork or to ever forget the saving power of Christ's blood shed on Calvary.

1. The Old Testament sacrificial system required a repetitious sacrifice and sprinkling of the blood of animals. The book of Hebrews explains the typology of that system and sums up the essence of the Old and New Covenants in Hebrews 9–10. According to Hebrews 9:13–14, 22, why was the shedding of blood necessary?
   Without the shedding of blood there is no remission for sins.

2. According to Hebrews 10:10–22, why are animal sacrifices no longer necessary?
   Jesus Christ, the Son of God, shed His blood once for all to pay for sin.

3. The number of red blood cells in the average person's body is immense—about 2.5×10^{13}. If the average diameter of a red blood cell is 7.5 μm = 7.5×10^{-6} m, how many times would a rope made up of this many red blood cells reach around the equator ($c = 40{,}075$ km)? Round to the nearest hundredth.
   4.68 times

4. If the total surface area of 2.5×10^{13} red blood cells is about 3,800 m², what would be the diameter of a ball with an equivalent surface area?
   $d = 34.8$ m

5. The white blood cells are like an army, constantly fighting invaders such as bacteria, viruses, fungi, and parasites. There are different types of white blood cells, each with a specialized function in the army. Their numbers fluctuate greatly since many die in "battle" with the "enemies." If, on average, there is about one white blood cell for each 800 red blood cells, about how many does a healthy human have?
   3.125×10^{10} white blood cells

But if we walk in the light, as he is in the light, we have fellowship one with another, and the blood of Jesus Christ his Son cleanseth us from all sin. 1 John 1:7

Surface Areas of Three-Dimensional Figures (Extra Practice; use after 13.6.)

Find the surface area of the following figures.

_____384 cm²_____ 1. a cube with an edge of 8 cm

_____280 in.²_____ 2. How much cardboard does it take to make a shoe box whose base is 10 in. × 6 in. and whose height is 4 in.? The lip of the lid is 1 in. tall.

_____$30\frac{3}{8}$ in.²_____ 3. a cube with $e = 2\frac{1}{4}$ in.

_____260 m²_____ 4. What is the lateral surface area of a right pyramid with a 10 m square base and a height of 12 m?

_____32π in.²_____ 5. How much tin does it take to make a tin can that is 4 in. in diameter and 6 in. high? (Express the answer in terms of π.)

_____63.5 ft.²_____ 6. Find the total surface area of a triangular prism whose height is 10 ft. and whose base is an equilateral triangle with sides of 2 ft. (Hint: Divide the bases into two congruent right triangles to find their areas.)

_____314 in.²_____ 7. How much leather is used to cover a volleyball that is 10 in. in diameter?

Find the missing measure.

_____$\frac{8}{\pi}$ in._____ 8. The lateral surface area of an 8 in. high right circular cylinder is 128 in.². Find the radius. (Express the answer in terms of π.)

_____$4\sqrt{5}$ cm_____ 9. What is the exact length of the edge of a cube covered with 480 cm² of material?

_____8 in._____ 10. A 10 ft. long piece of plastic pipe has to have a lateral surface area of 3,020 in.². Find the diameter (to the nearest inch).

Deltahedra   (Enrichment; use after 13.6.)

You have been studying some familiar polyhedra such as prisms and pyramids. There are actually five regular polyhedra, often referred to as the *Platonic solids*, after the Greek philosopher and mathematician Plato. A *regular polyhedron* must have congruent polygons for its faces, and all the angles at each vertex must be congruent. Three of the regular polyhedra have equilateral triangles for their faces. These figures are also called *deltahedra*, possibly because an equilateral triangle looks like the capital Greek letter delta (Δ). There are a total of eight deltahedra that can be constructed from equilateral triangles arranged in an appropriate net.

A net is a plane figure that can be folded into a three-dimensional figure. Enlarge the nets given for each of the Platonic solids, three of which are deltahedra. Fold them to create the three-dimensional figures shown.

1. regular tetrahedron: a four-sided deltahedron

Net

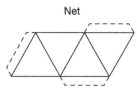

2. cube: a six-sided figure

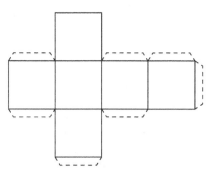

3. regular octahedron: an eight-sided deltahedron

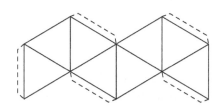

4. dodecahedron: a twelve-sided figure

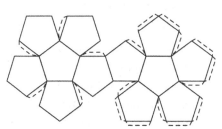

5. regular icosahedron: a twenty-sided deltahedron

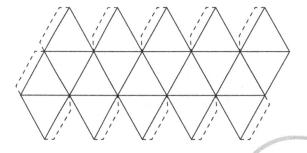

The nets for the other five convex deltahedra are given below. Enlarge the nets and fold them to create the three-dimensional figures shown. As you fold each figure, match the numbered vertices. Be sure to fold along every line before you start gluing or taping the figure into its final shape.

6. six-sided deltahedron (triangular dipyramid)

   The shape formed is two base-to-base tetrahedra.

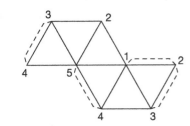 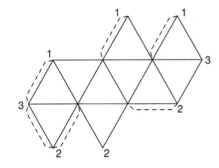

7. ten-sided deltahedron (pentagonal dipyramid)

   The shape formed is two pentagonal pyramids.

 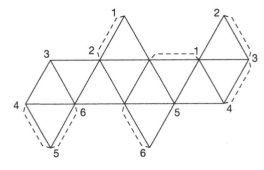

8. twelve-sided deltahedron (snub disphenoid)

   The shape formed looks like two regular octahedra with a pair of faces removed from each before they are joined together.

 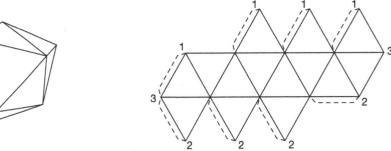

9. fourteen-sided deltahedron (triaugmented triangular prism)

   The shape formed looks like three square pyramids joined in pairs along one segment of each base, plus two triangle fillers.

10. sixteen-sided deltahedron (gyroelongated square dipyramid)

    The shape formed looks like two square pyramids with their bases joined by a zig-zag set of eight equilateral triangles.

  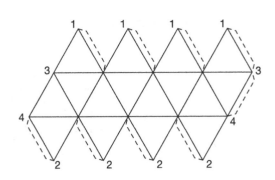

Volumes of Three-Dimensional Figures (Enhanced Practice; use after 13.8.)

Find the volume of the following figures. Use 3.14 for π and round to the nearest tenth where applicable.

_____ 512 cm³ _____   1. a cube with an edge of 8 cm

_____ 62.8 in.³ _____   2. a 5 in. tall can of peaches with a diameter of 4 in.

_____ 456.4 in.³ _____   3. a regulation basketball whose circumference is 30 in.

_____ 17,280 ft.³ _____   4. the interior of a 32 ft. × 60 ft. house with 9 ft. ceilings

_____ 167.5 cm³ _____   5. a cone-shaped drinking cup with a diameter of 8 cm and a height of 10 cm

_____ 720 m³ _____   6. a square pyramid measuring 12 m on a side with a height of 15 m

Find the missing measure.

_____7,180.8 gal._____ 7. How many gallons does a pool require if it is 8 ft. wide, 3 ft. deep, and 40 ft. long? (Hint: One cubic foot of water holds 7.48 gal.)

_____14.7 in._____ 8. Assuming that a 5 gal. bucket is a right circular cylinder with a 10 in. diameter, how tall is it? (Hint: 1 ft.^{3} = 1,728 in.^{3}.)

_____3,507.4 gal._____ 9. A mixing tank is a right circular cylinder with a 45° cone on the bottom. If the tank's radius is 4 ft. and it measures 12 ft. from the rim of the cylinder to the tip of the cone, how many gallons does it hold?

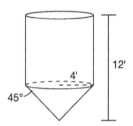

_____6 bags_____ 10. A set of four brick posts at the entry to a home will have caps that are square pyramids with bases 16 in. on a side and a height of 6 in. Each pyramid is poured as one piece with a base; the base is a prism that is also 16 in. on a side and 3 in. high. The homeowner plans to mix his own concrete using bags of mix. How many bags should he purchase if each makes 0.5 ft.^{3} of concrete?

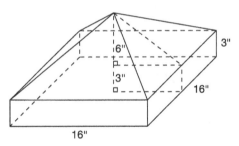

Chapter 13

Calculator Skill 13 (Use after 13.8.)

written for the TI-30Xa

Unit Analysis Conversions

Formulas are used in the calculation of areas and volumes. They express the relationships between certain dimensions using variables. Thus, algebra plays a role in the study of geometry. Geometry enables us to model things in the world around us, while algebra enables us to quantify those relationships in order to make important decisions.

Example 1

Use your calculator to find the acreage (area) of a horse pasture that is shaped like a trapezoid (1 acre = 43,560 ft.^{2}).

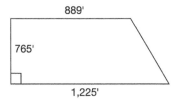

Answer

Substitute the given values into the formula: $A = \frac{1}{2}(b_1 + b_2)h = \frac{1}{2}(889 + 1{,}225)(765) = 808{,}605$ ft.^{2}.
To find the number of acres, divide by 43,560: $808{,}605 \div 43{,}560 \approx 18.56$ acres.
You can use the order of operations and your calculator to find the answer in one series of calculations: 889 ⊞ 1225 ⊟ ⊠ 765 ⊡ 2 ⊡ 43560 ⊟.

Example 2

The Great Pyramid of Cheops (Khufu) at Giza, Egypt, has a square base with sides measuring 230.33 m. It was originally 146.5 m high and contains about 1,300,000 blocks of limestone and marble weighing between 2.5 and 15 metric tons each. Find the volume of the Great Pyramid in cubic meters.

Answer

Substitute the given values into the formula: $A = \frac{1}{3}BH = \frac{1}{3}(230.33^2)(146.5) = 2{,}590{,}701.55$ m^3.
Use the order of operations and your calculator to find the answer: 230 ⊡ 33 ⊠² ⊠ 146 ⊡ 5 ⊡ 3 ⊟.

You can use unit analysis to convert measurements from one unit to another. First, determine equal quantities, such as 1 m = 3.28 ft. Then produce the needed ratio to cancel the given units and to introduce the desired units. For example, to convert meters to feet, multiply by 1 in the form of $\frac{3.28\ \text{ft.}}{1\ \text{m}}$ and simplify. Use your calculator to do the computations.

Example 3

Give the dimensions of the Great Pyramid in feet and the area of its base in acres.

Answer

$H = 146.5 \, \text{m} \left(\dfrac{3.28 \, \text{ft.}}{1 \, \text{m}} \right) = 480.52 \, \text{ft.}$

$s = 230.33 \, \text{m} \left(\dfrac{3.28 \, \text{ft.}}{1 \, \text{m}} \right) \approx 755.48 \, \text{ft.}$

$A = 755.48^2 = 570{,}750.03 \, \text{ft.}^2$

$A = 570{,}750.03 \, \text{ft.}^2 \left(\dfrac{1 \, \text{acre}}{43{,}560 \, \text{ft.}^2} \right) \approx 13.10 \, \text{acres}$

Use your calculator and the given equivalencies to perform the following unit analysis conversions.

1 mi. = 5,280 ft.	1 ft.^{2} = 144 in.^{2}
1 mi. = 1.609 km	1 yd.^{2} = 9 ft.^{2}
1 ft. = 0.305 m	1 acre = 43,560 ft.^{2}
1 in. = 2.54 cm	

_____3.73_____ 1. 6 km = ___ mi.

_____1.904_____ 2. 82,942 ft.^{2} = ___ acres

_____26.535_____ 3. 87 ft. = ___ m

_____1,030.4_____ 4. 9,274 ft.^{2} = ___ yd.^{2}

_____221,760_____ 5. 42 mi. = ___ ft.

_____2,496.82_____ 6. 983 in. = ___ cm

_____13,380.33_____ 7. 4,081 m = ___ ft.

_____41,299.6_____ 8. 104,901 cm = ___ in.

_____85,392_____ 9. 593 ft.^{2} = ___ in.^{2}

_____980.44_____ 10. 386 in. = ___ cm

Problem Solving—Area and Volume (Use after 13.8.)

Using the formulas from Chapter 13, solve the following problems. (Use 3.14 for π.)

1. You are given 1,000 ft. of rope, and you can use it to enclose a parcel of land that will be yours to keep. If the property must be a quadrilateral, what size and shape will you make the perimeter in order to get the maximum area in acres? Round to the nearest thousandth of an acre (1 acre = 43,560 ft.²).
   square with s = 250 ft. and A = 1.435 acres

2. Suppose the property in exercise 1 is enclosed within a circular shape. Would the area enclosed be greater or less than the area of the quadrilateral in exercise 1? By how much? Round to the nearest thousandth of an acre.
   0.393 acres greater

3. What percent of a cylindrical can holding three tennis balls is empty space? Each ball is $2\frac{9}{16}$ in. in diameter. Assume that the inside diameter of the can is the same as the outside diameter of a tennis ball. Round to the nearest tenth of a percent.
   33.3%

4. How much material (sheet plastic or aluminum) is needed to make a tennis ball can, including the lid? Round to the nearest thousandth.
   72.165 in.²

5. How many milliliters does a drinking straw hold if it has a diameter of 5 mm and is 20 cm long (1 cm³ = 1 mL)?
   3.925 mL

6. How many drinking straws like the one in exercise 5 would it take to hold an entire 2 L bottle of soda?
510 straws

7. A circular irrigation system consists of a 200 ft. long arm that rotates around a central point at the water source. The arm has a number of sprinkler heads and a series of wheels that it rolls on and is located in a square field that measures 400 ft. on a side. How many acres in the corners of the field do not get irrigated? What percent of the field is not irrigated? Round to the nearest hundredth of an acre and the nearest tenth of a percent.
0.79 acres; 21.5%

8. A math class decided to calculate the number of blades of grass on the football field. Fifteen sets of partners scattered across the field and counted how many blades were in 1 in.^{2} of the turf. The average of the fifteen results was 96 blades/in.^{2}. If the football field is 160 ft. × 360 ft., approximately how many blades of grass are on the field?
796,262,400 blades of grass

9. Randy wonders whether a waffle cone filled level with soft ice cream would hold as much as the two spherical scoops that are used for hard ice cream. The waffle cone has a diameter of 8 cm and an inside height of 14 cm, and the scoop has a diameter of 6.2 cm. Determine which option has more ice cream and how much more it has.
Two scoops are greater by about 15 cm^3.

Chapter 13 Review

Matching: Give the best answer.

a. rectangle
b. trapezoid
c. pyramid
d. cylinder
e. triangle

f. square
g. cone
h. parallelogram
i. prism

___e___ 1. a three-sided polygon

___h___ 2. a four-sided polygon with opposite sides parallel

___a___ 3. a parallelogram with four right angles

___f___ 4. a four-sided polygon with four right angles and four equal sides

___d___ 5. a three-dimensional figure with two congruent, parallel, circular bases

___b___ 6. a four-sided polygon with at least one pair of opposite sides parallel

___i___ 7. a three-dimensional figure with all faces flat surfaces and at least two congruent parallel faces

Matching: Give the geometric figure that matches each formula. All choices will be used. Some questions have more than one answer, so give all possible answers.

a. triangle
b. prism
c. pyramid
d. rectangle
e. cone

f. circle
g. trapezoid
h. parallelogram
i. cylinder

___a___ 8. $A = \frac{1}{2}bh$

___d, h___ 9. $A = bh$

___g___ 10. $A = \frac{1}{2}(b_1 + b_2)h$

___b, i___ 11. $V = BH$

___c, e___ 12. $V = \frac{1}{3}BH$

___f___ 13. $A = \pi r^2$

Find the area of the following figures. Use 3.14 for π and round to the nearest hundredth where applicable.

14. ___42 mm²___

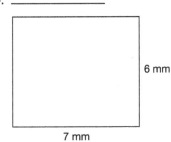

7 mm
6 mm

15. ___15 in.²___

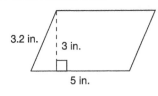

3.2 in.
3 in.
5 in.

16. ___165 ft.²___

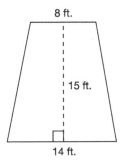

8 ft.
15 ft.
14 ft.

17. ___11.04 cm²___

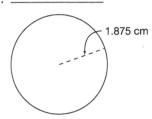

1.875 cm

___78.5 in.²___ 18. circle with $r = 5.0$ in.

___10.08 m²___ 19. parallelogram with $b = 4.2$ m and $h = 2.4$ m

___12.98 cm²___ 20. trapezoid with $b_1 = 3.2$ cm, $b_2 = 2.7$ cm, and $h = 4.4$ cm

___8 in.___ 21. Find the height of a triangle whose area is 64 in.² and whose base is 16 in.

Find the area of the following shaded regions. Use 3.14 for π and round to the nearest hundredth where applicable.

___390 mm²___ 22.

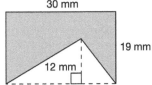

30 mm
19 mm
12 mm

___5.30 cm²___ 23. △ABC is an equilateral triangle 7 cm on a side. D, E, and F are midpoints. $CD = 6.06$ cm.

_287.5 m²_ 24.

20 m
5 m
15 m
10 m
25 m

_95.04 in.²_ 25.

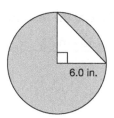

6.0 in.

423.12 cm² 26. $AP = 19$ cm and $AQ = 30$ cm

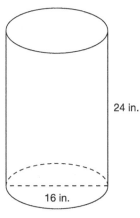

Q
P
O
A

2.86 cm² 27.

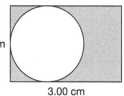

2.00 cm
3.00 cm

Solve. Round up to the next whole unit.

28. How many square yards of carpet are needed for a room 20 ft. by 25 ft.?
56 yd.²

29. If one gallon of paint covers 375 ft.², how many gallons must be purchased to paint a wall 75 ft. by 12 ft.?
3 gal.

Find the surface area of the following figures. Use 3.14 for π and round to the nearest hundredth where applicable.

30. _1,607.68 in.²_

24 in.
16 in.

31. _358.4 mm²_

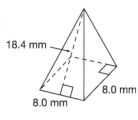

18.4 mm
8.0 mm
8.0 mm

32. _19.82 cm²_

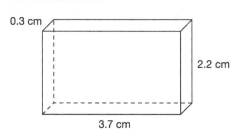

0.3 cm
2.2 cm
3.7 cm

33. _1,291 in.²_

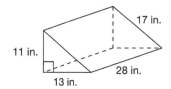

17 in.
11 in.
13 in.
28 in.

Find the volume of the following figures. Use 3.14 for π and round to the nearest tenth where applicable.

34. _____1,750 cm³_____

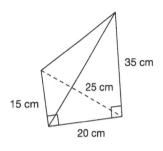

35. _____38.3 m³_____

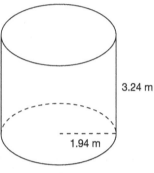

36. _____1,464,155.8 cm³_____

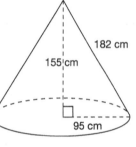

37. _____12,540 in.³_____

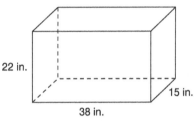

_____5 : 8_____ 38. The ratio of the sides of two similar parallelograms is 5 : 8. What is the ratio of their heights?

_____18 in._____ 39. The area of a triangle is 36 in.². The area of a similar triangle is 81 in.². If the base of the smaller triangle is 12 in., what is the length of the base of the larger triangle?

40. When the radius of a circle is tripled, what is the effect on the area?
    It is nine times as large.

Cumulative Review 13

<u>d</u> 1. Subtract $-84 - (-92)$.

  a. -8 d. 8
  b. 176   e. none of these
  c. -176

<u>e</u> 2. Solve $y + 8 = -23$.

  a. $y = -15$ d. $y = -184$
  b. $y = -\frac{23}{8}$ e. none of these
  c. $y = 15$

<u>b</u> 3. Find three consecutive integers such that the sum of the largest integer and three times the smallest integer is 14 more than twice the middle integer. Which of the following equations could be used to solve this problem?

  a. $x + 3x = 2x + 14$ d. $x + 3(x + 1) = 2x + 14$
  b. $(x + 2) + 3x = 2(x + 1) + 14$ e. none of these
  c. $x + 3x = 2(x + 2) - 14$

<u>a</u> 4. Chad can travel 156 mi. on his motorcycle on 3 gal. of gasoline. How many miles per gallon does he get?

  a. 52 mi./gal.   d. 48 mi./gal.
  b. 468 mi./gal.   e. none of these
  c. 19 mi./gal.

<u>d</u> 5. Divide $\frac{9}{7}$ by $\frac{27}{49}$.

  a. $\frac{3}{7}$ d. $\frac{7}{3}$
  b. $\frac{36}{56}$ e. none of these
  c. $\frac{243}{343}$

<u>b</u> 6. Solve $x - \frac{4}{5} = 2x + \frac{3}{5}$.

  a. $x = \frac{5}{7}$ d. $x = -\frac{1}{5}$
  b. $x = -\frac{7}{5}$ e. none of these
  c. $x = \frac{1}{5}$

<u>c</u> 7. Lydia's science grade changed from 72 to 85 over a six-week period. What is the percent change in her grade?

  a. 18.1% decrease   d. 15.3% decrease
  b. 15.3% increase   e. none of these
  c. 18.1% increase

_____e_____ 8. Solve $3x + 9 \geq 51$.

    a. $x \leq 14$ d. $x \geq 39$

    b. $x > 14$ e. none of these

    c. $x > 20$

_____d_____ 9. Solve $6x^2 + 7 = 103$.

    a. $x = -4$ d. $x = \pm 4$

    b. $x = \sqrt{110}$ e. none of these

    c. $x = 96$

_____d_____ 10. Find the hypotenuse of a right triangle with legs of 7 and 15.

    a. $\sqrt{176}$ d. $\sqrt{274}$

    b. 44   e. none of these

    c. $\sqrt{79}$

_____d_____ 11. If the length of a rectangle is 8 more than its width and its perimeter is 24, find the dimensions of the rectangle.

    a. 2×8 d. 2×10

    b. 8×16 e. none of these

    c. 4×8

_____a_____ 12. Which of the following describes two angles whose measures sum to 180°?

    a. supplementary angles   d. adjacent angles

    b. vertical angles   e. none of these

    c. complementary angles

_____a_____ 13. A nine-sided polygon is called what?

    a. nonagon   d. heptagon

    b. hexagon   e. none of these

    c. pentagon

_____c_____ 14. Find the distance between the points $(-7, 2)$ and $(3, 8)$.

    a. $\sqrt{106}$ d. $\sqrt{146}$

    b. $2\sqrt{29}$ e. none of these

    c. $2\sqrt{34}$

_____b_____ 15. One angle of a right triangle is 45°. If a leg of this triangle is 9 cm, how long is the hypotenuse?

    a. 9 cm   d. 18 cm

    b. $9\sqrt{2}$ cm   e. none of these

    c. $9\sqrt{3}$ cm

14 Polynomials

Creation Wonders—The Senses of Smell and Taste

(Bible Activity; use after 14.1.)

The human senses of smell and taste are intricately connected, and both require some interesting chemistry. Our ability to taste depends on our sense of smell, as all of us know from our experience with colds. The Bible has numerous references to taste and smell. In John 12:3 we read that Mary of Bethany, in an extravagant act of love, anointed the Lord Jesus with a costly ointment whose pleasant aroma filled the house. In Psalm 34:8 taste is used in a metaphoric reference. We are admonished to "taste and see that the Lord is good."

Even though we can distinguish more than ten thousand different scents, we find it difficult to describe what we smell, but our ability to remember a vast number of smells can usually last a lifetime. The olfactory mucous membrane contains millions of receptor cells that capture the odor-causing molecules and transmit "smell messages" to the brain. Our taste buds are not nearly as sensitive and transmit information based on only four tastes: sweet, sour, salty, and bitter. It requires 25,000 more molecules to taste a substance than it does to smell it. Most of us detect sweet tastes the best, tasting even as little as 1 µg (0.000001 g) of sugar diluted in 1 cm^3 of liquid. The interconnection between smell and taste also stimulates our salivary glands, hence the expression "mouth-watering smell" of, for example, chocolate chip cookies baking. We may like broccoli, but its smell does not cause the same pleasant response as the cookies' smell does. Our sense of smell is more sensitive than most scientific instruments, and we can detect certain odors in concentrations as little as 10^{-13} g/L. Two almost identical substances can smell quite different. D-carone smells like cumin, while its mirror-image counterpart L-carone smells like mint. We can only wonder at the truly remarkable gifts of smell and taste the Creator has designed for us.

1. Leviticus 2:2 and 6:15 describe a sacrificial offering as being a sweet savor to the Lord. What did the priests use to give the offering a sweet smell?

   frankincense

2. What other offering, mentioned in Ephesians 5:2, is described as being a sweet savor?

   Christ's sacrificial death

3. If there are about 20 million receptor cells in the nasal passages located in about 5 cm^2 of mucous membrane, what is their density per square millimeter?

   40,000/mm^2

4. Jesus ate food after His Resurrection (Luke 24:41–43; John 21:13). Also, a meal is mentioned in Revelation 19:9 that seems to indicate a continuation of our abilities to smell and taste after death. What is that meal?

   marriage supper of the Lamb

5. Why do you think God gave many poisonous substances and spoiled food an extremely bad taste or repugnant odor?

   for our protection

> *For we are unto God a sweet savour of Christ, in them that are saved, and in them that perish: to the one we are the savour of death unto death; and to the other the savour of life unto life. And who is sufficient for these things?* 2 Corinthians 2:15–16

Prime-Generating Polynomials   (Enrichment; use after 14.1.)

Leonhard Euler (*OIL er*) was one of the world's greatest mathematicians. He was born in 1707 in Switzerland into a religious family; his father was a Reformed pastor and his mother was a pastor's daughter. His father was a friend of the Bernoulli family, and the famous mathematician Johann Bernoulli influenced Euler greatly. By the age of 13 he was studying at the University of Basel, and he graduated with his master's degree in 1723 at the age of 16. In three more years he had earned a PhD.

Euler never wavered from the religious beliefs of his family throughout his life. He was a staunch Calvinist and defended his faith even to his employer Fredrick the Great, who was an atheist. He occasionally preached, and he led his family in daily worship. Although he and his wife had thirteen children, eight of them died in early childhood.

Because of a fever, Euler was blind in his right eye by the time he was 28. Later he developed a cataract on his left eye that caused him to become almost totally blind. He later stated that "only his faith in God enabled him to bear those days of torment."[1] Even in the face of extreme difficulty he continued his studies, writing numerous mathematical works.

One of Euler's interesting discoveries, made in 1772, was a polynomial that generates only prime numbers, $n^2 + n + 41$. Called a *prime-generating polynomial*, this polynomial gives forty distinct primes when it is evaluated using the consecutive integers $n = 0$ to $n = 39$. Prime-generating polynomials are still studied today. In 2000 Flannery and Flannery transformed Euler's polynomial into $n^2 - 79n + 1,601$ to produce a prime-generating polynomial that generates prime numbers from eighty consecutive integers.

[1]Dan Graves, *Scientists of Faith* (Grand Rapids: Kregel, 1996), 86.

Use a calculator to complete the following exercises.

1. Evaluate Euler's polynomial for integer values from 0 to 4.
   41, 43, 47, 53, 61

2. Verify that each of these numbers is a prime number.
   The only factors of each of these numbers are one and the number itself.

3. Legendre in 1798 transformed Euler's polynomial to $n^2 - n + 41$ and claimed that the same prime numbers could be obtained by evaluating his polynomial for integers from 1 to 40. Evaluate Legendre's prime-generating polynomial for integer values from 1 to 5. Do these values match your answers to exercise 1?
   41, 43, 47, 53, 61; yes

4. Mathematicians are still researching prime-generating polynomials. In 2006 Brox reported finding a polynomial that produced (possibly in absolute values) only primes for integer values, n, from 0 to 61. The Brox polynomial is $6n^2 - 342n + 4,903$. Find the first five prime numbers using this polynomial.
   4,903; 4,567; 4,243; 3,931; 3,631

Adding and Subtracting Polynomials (Extra Practice; use after 14.3.)

Add or subtract.

_____ $8x + 6$ _____ 1. $(3x + 6) + 5x$

_____ $2x^2 + x - 9$ _____ 2. $(2x^2 - 3x + 3) + (4x - 12)$

_____ $-5x^2 + 7x - 8$ _____ 3. $(-2x^2 + 5x - 9) - (3x^2 - 2x - 1)$

_____ $3y^2 + 2y + 14$ _____ 4. $(7y + 15) - (-3y^2 + 5y + 1)$

_____ $9x^4 + 5x^3 - 10x^2 + 10$ _____ 5. $(8x^4 + 2x^3 - 9x^2 + 12) + (x^4 + 3x^3 - x^2 - 2)$

_____ $\frac{3}{2}x^2 - \frac{7}{20}$ _____ 6. $\left(\frac{2}{3}x^2 - \frac{3}{5}\right) + \left(\frac{5}{6}x^2 + \frac{1}{4}\right)$

_____ $-x^2 + 2$ _____ 7. $(4x^2 + 13) + (2x^2 - 9) - (7x^2 + 2)$

_____ $14z^3 + 7z^2 - 9z$ _____ 8. $(12z^3 + 7z^2 - 18z) + (2z^3 + 9z)$

_____ $\frac{7}{8}y^3 - \frac{9}{2}y^2 + \frac{1}{12}y + \frac{23}{4}$ _____ 9. $\left(\frac{1}{2}y^3 - 5y^2 + \frac{5}{12}y + 6\right) + \left(\frac{3}{8}y^3 + \frac{1}{2}y^2 - \frac{1}{3}y - \frac{1}{4}\right)$

_____ $2.1x^2 - 5x + 7.2$ _____ 10. $(4.2x^2 - 3.5x + 5.2) - (2.1x^2 + 1.5x - 2)$

_____ $2x^3 + 15x^2 - 22x + 4$ _____ 11. $(13 + 4x^3 - 16x + 7x^2) - (2x^3 + 9 - 8x^2 + 6x)$

_____ $16x^3 + 19x^2 - 12x$ _____ 12. $(24x^2 + 2x) + (12x^3 - 5x^2) - (14x - 4x^3)$

_____ $-5x^3 + 14x^2 - 16x + 32$ _____ 13. $(4x + 12) - (x^2 + 20x) + (20 - 3x^3) - (2x^3 - 15x^2)$

_____ 4 _____ 14. $(21x^2 + 9x - 11) - 3(7x^2 + 3x - 5)$

Calculator Skill 14 (Use after 14.3.)

written for the TI-30Xa

Functional Values

Finding the value of a function $y = f(x)$ for a given value of x_1 means to substitute the x_1 value into the function and find the corresponding y value. The notation for evaluating a function at x_1 is written $f(x_1)$. Determining the functional values of a polynomial is actually an order of operations problem. Remember to evaluate exponents before doing the other four basic operations.

Example 1

Find $f(2)$ for the polynomial function $f(x) = 3x^3 - 7x^2 + 15x - 9$.

Answer

Substitute 2 in place of x in the polynomial: $f(2) = 3(2^3) - 7(2^2) + 15(2) - 9$.

Keystrokes: 3 ⊠ 2 [yˣ] 3 ⊟ 7 ⊠ 2 [x²] ⊞ 15 ⊠ 2 ⊟ 9 ⊟

Result: 17

Example 2

Find $P(-2.1526)$ for the polynomial function $P(x) = 1.368x^3 + 4.524x^2 - 12.42x$.

Answer

First store the x value in memory ① so you don't have to reenter it each time.

Keystrokes: 2 ⊡ 1526 [+⊃−] [STO] ①

Substitute −2.1526 in place of x in the polynomial:
$P(-2.1526) = 1.368(-2.1526)^3 + 4.524(-2.1526)^2 - 12.42(-2.1526)$.

Keystrokes: 1 ⊡ 368 ⊠ [RCL] ① [yˣ] 3 ⊞ 4 ⊡ 524 ⊠ [RCL] ① [x²] ⊟ 12 ⊡ 42 ⊠ [RCL] ① ⊟

Result: 34.05301031

Find the following functional values.

32.08	1. Find $f(7.1)$ for $f(x) = 2.8x + 12.2$.
112.24055	2. Find $f(2.55)$ for $f(x) = 4.22x^2 - 14x + 120.5$.
−174,789.1491	3. Find $f(-24.35)$ for $f(x) = 12.3x^3 + 4.68x^2 - 1.22x - 10.48$.
1.53×10^8	4. Find $f(3.2 \times 10^5)$ for $f(x) = (5.25 \times 10^2)x - (1.5 \times 10^7)$.
7,589,086.5	5. Find $f(-563.25)$ for $f(x) = 24x^2 + 44x - 144$.
−0.1079703	6. Find $f(0.0025)$ for $f(x) = 0.0124x^3 - 0.048x^2 + 0.012x - 0.108$.
178,812.2373	7. Find $f(7.25)$ for $f(x) = 518.35x^3 - 356.14x^2$.
0	8. Find $f(2.5)$ for $f(x) = x^2 + 5.3x - 19.5$.
0	9. Find $f(-7.8)$ for $f(x) = x^2 + 5.3x - 19.5$.
8.2	10. If $f(x_0) = 30.23$ for $f(x) = 5.25x - 12.82$, what is the value of x_0?

Problem Solving—Multiple Strategies (Use after 14.4.)

For each problem, devise a plan for finding the solution, carry out the plan, and then check your answer.

1. When surveyors want to find a distance where the line of sight is blocked, they measure it indirectly. They make the unknown distance one side of a triangle whose other two sides they can measure. If you don't have surveying equipment, you can still use this method by making the two measurable distances the sides of a right triangle. To find the distance across a forested area, Roger formed a right triangle around it and got 390 ft. for one leg and 468 ft. for the other leg. To the nearest foot, how far is it across the forested area?
   609 ft.

2. On a business trip a salesman found that he averaged 72 mi./hr. going to his destination but only 36 mi./hr. on the return trip over the same road due to an accident and a construction area. What was his average speed for the roundtrip? The well-known formula $d = rt$ can be used to find the rate, but the roundtrip rate must be the total distance divided by the total time.
   48 mi./hr.

3. Alyssa and Stacy are working on decorations for the large front entrance of the church. The four columns, which are 12 in. in diameter and 25 ft. tall, will be wound with garland strings that make a complete loop around each column for every 6 in. of vertical height. What is the minimum length of garland they will need for these four columns? Round the circumference up to the nearest inch and the final answer to the nearest foot.
   7,600 in. ≈ 633 ft.

4. The city of León is planning to repave all the roads in its business district, so the city council needs to determine the number of square meters of road to be paved for the cost estimate. There are twelve city blocks, each measuring 150 m × 64 m. The roads are all 16 m wide. The five avenues run with the long dimension of the city blocks, and the four streets run with the short dimension. Make a sketch and find the total area of new paving needed. Be careful not to figure the intersections twice.
   57,504 m²

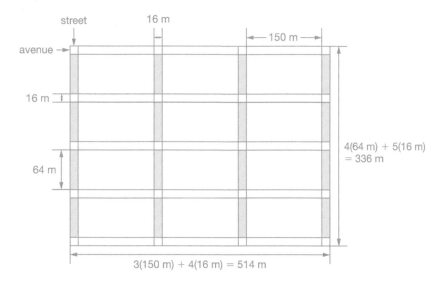

Multiplying Binomials (Enhanced Practice; use after 14.5.)

Use the FOIL method to multiply the following binomials. Remember to combine like terms.

_____ $20a^2 + 19a - 28$ _____ 1. $(4a + 7)(5a - 4)$

_____ $2x^2 - 3xy - 2y^2$ _____ 2. $(x - 2y)(2x + y)$

_____ $-15w^2 + 191w + 120$ _____ 3. $(40 - 3w)(3 + 5w)$

_____ $x^3y - xy^3$ _____ 4. $(xy^2 + x^2y)(x - y)$

_____ $30y^2 - 104y - 64$ _____ 5. $(2y - 8)(15y + 8)$

_____ $3x^2 + 10xy + 8y^2$ _____ 6. $(x + 2y)(3x + 4y)$

_____ $x^4 + 6x^2 - 72$ _____ 7. $(x^2 + 12)(x^2 - 6)$

_____ $24z^2 - 143z + 80$ _____ 8. $(16 - 3z)(5 - 8z)$

_____ $20x^2 - 180x + 405$ _____ 9. $5(2x - 9)^2$

_____ $108y^2 + 432y + 432$ _____ 10. $12(3y + 6)^2$

The FOIL method is actually an application of the Distributive Property. This same concept can be used to multiply a binomial by a trinomial. Every term in the binomial is distributed to every term of the trinomial, and then like terms are combined.

Example
Multiply $(x + 2)(x^2 - 4x + 7)$.

Answer
Distribute each term of $(x + 2)$ into the trinomial. Simplify and combine like terms.

$(x + 2)(x^2 - 4x + 7)$
$= x(x^2) - x(4x) + x(7) + 2(x^2) - 2(4x) + 2(7)$
$= x^3 - 4x^2 + 7x + 2x^2 - 8x + 14$
$= x^3 - 2x^2 - x + 14$

Use the Distributive Property to multiply each binomial by a trinomial.

_____ $10x^3 + 36x^2 + 54x - 28$ _____ 11. $(5x - 2)(2x^2 + 8x + 14)$

_____ $x^3 - y^3$ _____ 12. $(x - y)(x^2 + xy + y^2)$

_____ $8a^2 + 11ab - 2a + 3b^2 - 2b$ _____ 13. $(a + b)(8a + 3b - 2)$

_____ $m^3 - 10m + 12$ _____ 14. $(m - 2)(m^2 + 2m - 6)$

_____ $y^3 - 2y^2 + 2y + 5$ _____ 15. $(y + 1)(y^2 - 3y + 5)$

Multiplying and Dividing by Monomials (Extra Practice; use after 14.6.)

Multiply or divide.

_____ $15x^3$ _____   1. $5x(3x^2)$

_____ $32y^5$ _____   2. $-4y^2(-8y^3)$

_____ $-24z^7$ _____   3. $2z^3(-12z^4)$

_____ $7x^2y$ _____   4. $\dfrac{21x^2y^3}{3y^2}$

_____ $96x^5y^5$ _____   5. $6xy(4x^2y^2)^2$

_____ $-3a^2b^2$ _____   6. $\dfrac{-51a^3b^5}{17ab^3}$

_____ $24x^6 - 16x^5 - 96x^3$ _____   7. $8x^3(3x^3 - 2x^2 - 12)$

_____ $-6x^4y^2 - 24x^3y^3 + 15x^3y^2$ _____   8. $-3x^2y(8xy^2 + 2x^2y - 5xy)$

_____ $2x^3 - 6x$ _____   9. $\dfrac{18x^4 - 54x^2}{9x}$

_____ $3w^2z + 8wz^3 - 5$ _____   10. $\dfrac{32w^3z^6 - 20w^2z^3 + 12w^4z^4}{4w^2z^3}$

_____ $2x - 10y$ _____   11. $\dfrac{6xy(3x^2y - 15xy^2)}{9x^2y^2}$

Using Algebra (Extra Practice; use after 14.7.)

Write an equation and solve.

1. If x is the number of dimes in a stack of one hundred nickels and dimes, write an expression for the number of nickels. If the coins are worth $6.65, how many coins of each type are in the stack?

   nickels = 100 − x; 10x + 5(100 − x) = 665; 33 dimes and 67 nickels

2. A 24 oz. can of mixed peanuts and cashews costs $3.36. If the peanuts cost $1.60/lb. and the cashews cost $2.56/lb., how much of each type of nut is in the mixture? (Hint: Find the cost per ounce before writing an equation.)

   peanuts cost $0.10/oz. and cashews cost $0.16/oz.; 10p + 16(24 − p) = 336; 8 oz. of peanuts and 16 oz. of cashews

3. A global balanced fund has a stock-to-bond ratio of 40 : 1 (40 shares of stock for every bond). If the fifty bonds have an average value of $960, write an expression for the number of stocks and find the value of the fund if the average price of a share of stock is $25. What percent of the value of the fund is in bonds, and what percent is in stocks?

   stocks = 40(50) = 2,000 shares; 960(50) + 25(2,000) = $98,000; 49% in bonds and 51% in stocks

4. Eric had his $420 paycheck split into fives, tens, and twenties. He later noticed that there were twice as many tens as twenties and three times as many fives as tens. How many of each bill did he get from his paycheck?

   5(6x) + 10(2x) + 20x = 420; 6 twenties, 12 tens, and 36 fives

5. There are six coins in the United States monetary system, including a $1 coin. Starting at a penny, Bruce laid out a sequence of coins in an order that followed the Fibonacci sequence. How much money is his Fibonacci coin set worth?

   1(0.01) + 1(0.05) + 2(0.10) + 3(0.25) + 5(0.50) + 8(1) = $11.51

6. Cassandra has $99.35 in her purse. She has the same number of ones as she does twenties, but she has one fewer five than twenties. She also has two coins. What are her coins and how many of each bill does she have?

   x + 5(x − 1) + 20x = 99; 4 ones, 3 fives, and 4 twenties, plus a quarter and a dime

7. Besides his real estate, Scott has two IRAs, one certificate of deposit (CD), and a checking account. He noticed that, in round numbers, he has half as much in the smaller IRA as in the larger and that he has one-fifth as much in his CD as in the smaller IRA. If he has one-tenth as much in checking as in his CD, and his total amount of money is $161,000, how much is in each fund?

   $x + \frac{1}{2}x + \frac{1}{5}\left(\frac{1}{2}\right)x + \frac{1}{10}\left[\frac{1}{5}\left(\frac{1}{2}\right)\right]x = 161{,}000$; $100,000 in the larger IRA, $50,000 in the smaller IRA, $10,000 in the CD, and $1,000 in checking

Chapter 14

Chapter 14 Review

Give the degree of the following polynomials and identify the type of polynomial by special name. If no special name applies, write "polynomial." If it is not a polynomial, write "not a polynomial."

___2; binomial___ 1. $4x^2 - 7$

___0; monomial___ 2. 15

___3; trinomial___ 3. $6y^3 + 3y^2 - y$

___not a polynomial___ 4. $a^{-3} + 12$

___1; polynomial___ 5. $m + n - q + 3$

Evaluate the following polynomials when $x = -2$ and $y = 8$.

___2___ 6. $3x + y$

___312___ 7. $-2x^2 + 5y^2$

___80___ 8. $4(x^2 + 3xy + y^2)$

___-480___ 9. $x^2y - y^3$

Perform the indicated operations.

___$x^2 - 3x + 16$___ 10. $(3x^2 + 7) - (2x^2 + 3x - 9)$

___$7x^2 + 9x - 10$___ 11. $(4x^2 + 9x + 2) + (3x^2 - 12)$

___$9x^2 + 12x - 75$___ 12. $6(x^2 + 2x - 9) + 3(x^2 - 7)$

___$-9a - 19b + c$___ 13. $-4(2a + 6b - c) - (a - 5b + 3c)$

___$15ab^3$___ 14. $3b^2(5ab)$

___$-27x^3y - 108x^2y^3$___ 15. $-9x^2y(3x + 12y^2)$

$21a^4b^2 + 28a^3b^3 + 14a^3b^2$ 16. $7a^3b^2(3a + 4b + 2)$

$x^2 + 8x + 12$ 17. $(x + 6)(x + 2)$

$y^2 - 13y + 36$ 18. $(y - 4)(y - 9)$

$a^2 + a - 42$ 19. $(a + 7)(a - 6)$

$z^2 + 9z + 8$ 20. $(z + 1)(z + 8)$

$b^2 - 4b + 3$ 21. $(b - 3)(b - 1)$

$2x^2 - 16x + 24$ 22. $(2x - 4)(x - 6)$

$y^2 + 8y + 16$ 23. $(y + 4)(y + 4)$

$m^2 - 4m + 4$ 24. $(m - 2)(m - 2)$

$x^2 - 2x - 3$ 25. $(x + 1)(x - 3)$

_____$64x^6y^3$_____ 26. $(4x^2y)^3$

_____$x^2 - 12x + 36$_____ 27. $(x - 6)^2$

_____$6x^2 - x - 35$_____ 28. $(3x + 7)(2x - 5)$

_____$3ab$_____ 29. $\dfrac{9a^2b}{3a}$

_____$6xy^3$_____ 30. $\dfrac{-24x^2y^3z}{-4xz}$

_____$\dfrac{n^4}{5m^3}$_____ 31. $\dfrac{5m^2n^5}{25m^5n}$

_____$x^2 + 3y^2$_____ 32. $\dfrac{3x^2 + 9y^2}{3}$

_____$-4a - \dfrac{2b^2}{a} - \dfrac{1}{a}$_____ 33. $\dfrac{-24a^2 - 12b^2 - 6}{6a}$

_____$14xy^2 + 4y^2 - 12y$_____ 34. $\dfrac{42x^2y^3 + 12xy^3 - 36xy^2}{3xy}$

_____$\dfrac{a}{2} - \dfrac{1}{a} + \dfrac{3}{a^2} - 2$_____ 35. $\dfrac{7a^3 - 28a^2 - 14a + 42}{14a^2}$

Write an equation and solve.

36. Jeremy has 19 more dimes than nickels in his coin collection. If he has a total of 97 dimes and nickels, how many of each does he have?

    39 nickels and 58 dimes

37. Lydia's sister said, "I counted the number of coins in my piggy bank, and there are 85 coins. I have three more pennies than quarters, four times as many dimes as pennies, and seven more nickels than quarters." Can Lydia determine how many of each coin is in her sister's bank? If so, how many pennies, dimes, nickels, and quarters are in it?

    yes; 12 pennies, 16 nickels, 48 dimes, and 9 quarters

38. Luke has a total of $59 in his billfold. If he has three fewer ones than fives and twice as many ones as tens, how many of each bill does he have?

    4 ones, 7 fives, and 2 tens

39. Faith Christian Elementary had a loose change offering at chapel one Friday and collected $13.90. The offering was made up of 196 dimes and nickels. How many of each coin was in the offering that day?

    82 dimes and 114 nickels

40. Jacob cashed his $297 paycheck and received two more than twice as many twenties as tens. He also received four fewer fives than tens and two ones. How many of the larger bills did he receive?

    12 twenties, 5 tens, and 1 five

Cumulative Review 14

_____a_____ 1. Which of the following is not a function?
        a. $\{(4, 7), (-6, 4), (4, 9), (8, 2)\}$ d. $\{(-9, 1), (2, 1), (7, 1)\}$
        b. $\{(1, 1), (4, 4), (7, 4)\}$ e. none of these
        c. $\{(-1, 14), (14, -1), (3, 8), (8, 3)\}$

_____d_____ 2. Find the slope of the line passing through $(-7, 12)$ and the origin.
        a. $-\frac{7}{12}$ d. $-\frac{12}{7}$
        b. $\frac{-7}{-12}$ e. none of these
        c. $\frac{5}{12}$

_____c_____ 3. Find the slope-intercept form of the line passing through points $(5, 9)$ and $(7, 13)$.
        a. $y = -2x + 1$ d. $y = \frac{10}{3}x + \frac{17}{3}$
        b. $y = \frac{1}{2}x + \frac{13}{2}$ e. none of these
        c. $y = 2x - 1$

_____e_____ 4. What is the mean of $\{25, 38, 29, 32, 35, 33, 27, 32\}$?
        a. 29   d. 31.9
        b. 30.55   e. none of these
        c. 28.6

_____d_____ 5. What is the median of $\{25, 38, 29, 32, 35, 33, 27, 32\}$?
        a. 29   d. 32
        b. 30   e. none of these
        c. 29.5

_____a_____ 6. What is the mode of $\{25, 38, 29, 32, 35, 33, 27, 32\}$?
        a. 32   d. 30
        b. 35   e. none of these
        c. 25

_____b_____ 7. What is the lower quartile of $\{25, 38, 29, 32, 35, 33, 27, 32\}$?
        a. 29   d. 30
        b. 28   e. none of these
        c. 32

_____b_____ 8. Find the number of ways seven out of twelve books can be arranged on a shelf.
        a. 792   d. 5,040
        b. 3,991,680   e. none of these
        c. 84

<u>a</u>   9. Simplify $\sqrt{15,435}$.

     a. $21\sqrt{35}$ d. $245\sqrt{5}$

     b. $15\sqrt{7}$ e. none of these

     c. $10\sqrt{35}$

<u>c</u>   10. Simplify $\sqrt{80} + \sqrt{28} - \sqrt{180}$.

     a. $10\sqrt{5} + 2\sqrt{7}$ d. $\sqrt{35}$

     b. $\sqrt{2}$ e. none of these

     c. $-2\sqrt{5} + 2\sqrt{7}$

<u>b</u>   11. Simplify $\sqrt[3]{4,096}$.

     a. 8   d. 32

     b. 16   e. none of these

     c. 2^{12}

<u>a</u>   12. What is the complement of 74°?

     a. 16°   d. 29°

     b. 164°   e. none of these

     c. 106°

<u>d</u>   13. The three most basic geometric figures are the point, the line, and which of the following?

     a. triangle   d. plane

     b. square   e. none of these

     c. ray

<u>b</u>   14. $\triangle ABC \cong \triangle XYZ$. Complete the statement: $\overline{AC} \cong$ ___.

     a. $\overline{XY}$ d. $\overline{BC}$

     b. $\overline{XZ}$ e. none of these

     c. $\overline{YZ}$

<u>d</u>   15. Find the area of an isosceles right triangle if a leg is 14 in.

     a. 196 in.²   d. 98 in.²

     b. $98\sqrt{2}$ in.²   e. none of these

     c. $28 + 14\sqrt{2}$ in.